BOOKS BY MAURICE DRUON

The Glass Coffin and Other Stories
The Curtain Falls
The Film of Memory
Alexander the God

THE ACCURSED KINGS

The Iron King
The Strangled Queen
The Poisoned Crown
The Royal Succession
The She-Wolf of France
The Lily and the Lion

FOR CHILDREN

Tistou of the Green Thumbs

THE MEMOIRS OF ZEUS

Maurice Druon

THE MEMOIRS
OF ZEUS

TRANSLATED FROM THE FRENCH

by Humphrey Hare

CHARLES SCRIBNER'S SONS · NEW YORK

PRINTED IN THE UNITED STATES OF AMERICA

Library of Congress Catalog Card Number 64–14661

DECORATIONS BY JAMES AND RUTH MAC CREA

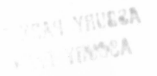

Contents

vii

A Concordance of
the Principal Divinities

GREEK		ROMAN
Aphrodite	Daughter of Uranus. Goddess of Love.	*Venus*
Apollo	Son of Zeus and Leto. God of Poetry, of Oracles, and of Music.	*Phoebus*
Ares	Son of Zeus and Hera. God of War.	*Mars*
Artemis	Twin sister of Apollo. Goddess of the Hunt and Chastity.	*Diana*
Athena	Daughter of Zeus and Metis. Goddess of Wisdom.	*Minerva*
Chaos	Ancestor of the world. Sometimes compared to	*Janus*
Charities	Daughters of Zeus and Eurynome.	*Graces*
Cronus	A Titan. Son of Uranus and Gæa. Second king of the gods. Father of Zeus.	*Saturn*
Demeter	Daughter of Zeus. Goddess of Agriculture and Fertility.	*Ceres*
Dionysis	Son of Zeus and Semele. God of Wine and Inspiration.	*Bacchus*

A CONCORDANCE OF THE PRINCIPAL DIVINITIES

GREEK		ROMAN
Erinys	Daughters of Uranus. Divinities of Vengeance and of Punishment.	*Furies*
Eros	Son of Chaos and Night. God of Love. Compared to	*Cupid*
Gæa	The Earth. Wife of Uranus. Mother of the Titans. Compared to	*Tellus Mater*
Hades	The Invisible. Brother of Zeus. God of the Lower World and of Underground Riches.	*Pluto*
Hebe	Daughter of Zeus and Hera. Personification of Youth.	*no equivalent*
Hecate	Daughter of Perses and Asteria. Goddess of Magic.	*no equivalent*
Hephaestus	Son of Zeus and Hera. Husband of Aphrodite. Divine blacksmith. God of Celestial Fire.	*Vulcan*
Hera	Sister and wife of Zeus. Goddess of Marriage.	*Juno*
Heracles	Son of Zeus and Alcmene.	*Hercules*
Hermes	Son of Zeus and Maia. Herald of the gods. Protector of Commerce, Trade and Travel. God of the Thieves. Inventor of Language.	*Mercury*
Hesperides	Daughters of Zeus and Themis. Guardians of the sacred gardens.	*Hesperides*

A CONCORDANCE OF THE PRINCIPAL DIVINITIES

GREEK		ROMAN
Hestia	Sister of Zeus. Goddess of the Hearth.	*Vesta*
Hours	Daughters of Zeus and Themis. Divinities of Agriculture and City Administration.	*Seasons*
Ilithia	Daughter of Zeus and Hera. Goddess of Childbirth. Attributes confused with	*Juno*
Iris	Messenger of the gods.	*Iris*
Metis	Prudence. Daughter of Oceanus and Tethys.	*no equivalent*
Mnemosyne	Memory. A Titaness. Daughter of Uranus and Gæa. Mother of the Muses.	*no equivalent*
Moirae	Daughters of Zeus and Themis. Guardians of individual destinies.	*no equivalent*
Muses	Daughters of Zeus and Mnemosyne. Goddesses of Arts and Sciences.	*Muses*
Oceanus	A Titan. Son of Uranus and Earth. God of Water, father of Rivers.	*no equivalent*
Pan	Son of Uranus. God of the Shepherds and Sexuality.	*Faunus*
Persephone	Daughter of Zeus and Demeter. Wife of Hades.	*Proserpina*
Poseidon	Son of Zeus. God of the Sea.	*Neptune*
Prometheus	Son of the Titan Iapetus. Cousin of Zeus.	*Prometheus*

GREEK		ROMAN
Rhea	A Titaness. Daughter of Uranus and Gæa. Sister and wife of Cronus. Mother of Zeus.	*Cybele*
Themis	A Titaness. Daughter of Uranus and Gæa. Goddess of the Law.	*no equivalent*
Uranus	The Sky. Husband of Earth. Father of the Titans, of the Cyclopes, of the nymphs, of the giants, of the centaurs, etc. Creator of men. Grandfather of Zeus. First king of the gods.	*no equivalent*
Zeus	Grandson of Uranus and of the Earth. Son of Cronus and Rhea. King of the gods.	*Jupiter*

THE MEMOIRS OF ZEUS

An Address to Mortals.

I, Zeus, have had a long sleep.

But, mortals, I have recently been awakened by certain disturbances among the clouds, which I knew to be your work. Raising my eyelids, I looked at the Earth; and I saw little on it that was new.

During my night of two thousand years no mountain has vanished; the rivers still flow towards the same seas, eating always a little deeper into the outer curves of their beds; and certain channels in deltas have silted up. The cuttle-fish still squirts the same sepia ink when attacked; the butterflies still carry on their wings the powder my grandfather spread; the bull still has a swelling at the seventh cervical; and the asphodel still waves its plumes on the slopes of the same hills.

Nor, indeed, among you men, can your unsatiable ingenuity, your outbursts of murderous aggression and your destestable tendency to pyromania be considered as anything new. Alas, I know only too well from whom you have inherited these things.

Your most recent conquests over space, gravity and time may seem to you immense and fill you with pride; but contemplated from where I see them, they assume smaller proportions.

You are still incapable of changing yourselves by your own efforts into gods. None of you has discovered how to infuse life into marble; and when you think you have made a lake you have to watch the dam night and day, for fear it burst and drown you.

While extending your range of action you have neither found true liberty nor, increasing your anxieties, have you been able to control your environment.

On the other hand you seem to have forgotten much.

You, mortals, to whom I am addressing these words, think of the gods, whenever it still occurs to you to think of them, as seated on thrones of glory, or lying voluptuously on beds of flowers listlessly inhaling the incense of praise and enjoying the delights of endless time in circumambient bliss.

Mortals, dear mortals, you are wrong. Do not confound what you would like to be with what we are. Life is no easier for a god than it is for the man in the street.

I, Zeus, king of gods, god of kings, am going to tell you my story.

THE FIRST EPOCH

Sky and Time

Origins.
Ancestor Chaos.
The Dreams of Gæa &
the Appearance of Uranus.

I belong to the third divine generation. The founder of our race was my grandfather Uranus, king of the Atlantes.

Before him a distant ancestor is mentioned, called Chaos, who mated with the female Void, the nocturnal matrix of worlds, and, from his scattered seed, engendered the primordial elements of the universe as well as the principal stars of our galaxy. Then, leaving to the most active of his sons, Eros, the duty of carrying on his work and controlling the combinations of the elements, Chaos withdrew into the Aether, whose name he took, there to sleep, or perhaps to prepare, with a slow and monstrous erection, the populating of another sidereal vacuity. But all this is very vague and hazy.

Even of the birth of Uranus no certain information has been handed down to me.

My grandmother Gæa, the Earth, maintained for a long time that she had given him birth without the intervention of any male principle, wishing to be the maker of her own husband. But my grandmother the Earth was always slightly mad about matters of conception and maternity. She was the first, but not the only, member of a long line of females who proudly dream of conceiving on their own, and become delirious at the mere thought of giving birth to beings who are the exclusive fruit of the maternal womb. These goddesses condemn themselves to chastity or to Amazonian amours, such as my daughter Artemis, or again to falling in love—and with what an excessive and tortured love—with their first-born son. Some avenge themselves by affecting to treat their indispensable husband as a mere brat. As for mortal women of this sort, they have at least the resource, in order to sublimate a copulation that offends them and a sharing which humiliates them, of calling on the desire of a god or of pretending they have submitted to it. How many have I assisted, and how many have I permitted to lie! And how my sons, Ares, Apollo, Heracles and Dionysus exerted themselves to appease in these beautiful, and sometimes ugly women their insane regret at not having been endowed with a double sex!

Oh, my daughters, my daughters, do not envy the fate of the oyster! If you only knew how bored the oyster is at having no one to attract but itself, and how infinitely melancholy its solitary nuptials are!

But let us return to Uranus.

He himself said he was the son of the Day and the Night, which was his way of revealing nothing at all.

One may well wonder whether he did not come from elsewhere, I mean from some other and distant region of the cosmos, where the divine powers were more advanced.

Whether it was due to a spirit of adventure, to a quarrel with his family, or to a voyage of exploration from which he had no means of returning, he took possession of the still virgin Earth and made her fecund. We, his grandchildren, have never been able to pierce the fog of mystery which surrounds his origins and adds to his greatness and majesty.

He was an admirable and excellent god, the master of all things, industrious, active, continuously breathing energy into all about him, authoritarian, but careful to be just and to dispense happiness.

My aunt Memory has often told me that I resemble her father in many ways. If I have inherited some of Uranus's virtues, it is surely these which have cut me out to be king of the gods.

The Children &
Works of Uranus.
Number & Creation.

The celestial Uranus had forty-five children by the Earth, the most important of whom were the six Titans, including my uncle Oceanus, the eldest, and my father Cronus, the youngest, and the six Titanides, including my mother Rhea and my aunt Memory; then followed the three great Cyclopes or One-Eyed, and the three Hecatoncheires, or Hundred-Handed. His progeny also included the nymphs of the first generation, and various gods, goddesses and giants of whom I shall tell you later.

Titans and Titanides had the power to reproduce themselves; the One-Eyed and the Hundred-Handed had not. But the Hundred-Handed each had fifty heads. Imagine the speed of calculation, the power of investigation of those combined fifty heads functioning on the same impulse; imagine the multiplicity, the prodigious strength or delicacy of action communicated to their five hundred fingers. As for the One-Eyed, directed by their single vision to their task, from which no temptation could distract them, they carried the crucibles from the fire and were in charge of the blow-lamps of the lightning.

You are thinking, mortals, of the most recent machines born of your ingenious researches, and you marvel at the fact that they reply quicker than you can yourselves to the questions you ask them, reproducing your gestures with an hundredfold efficiency, or concentrating invisible energies for your service. But take care not to draw over-hasty comparisons! Between your robots and the divine giants there is much the same difference as there is between you and me. And remember, too, that the Titans, Cyclopes and Hecatoncheires are immortal; I have chained them up in the somnolence of the depths of the world, but they can be awakened; and even their dreams are to be feared.

With his sons' help, Uranus built mountains and glaciers, here made glowing lava flow to establish his foundations, elsewhere spread thick beds of alluvium, everywhere crystallized the impalpable and concentrated the viscous, distributed the treasure of metals, and imposed on Pontus of the Sea, a descendant of Chaos, a law of harmony.

Of all these works, the great hydraulic system of the fecundating rain, so simple yet so perfect, indefinitely renewing its own rotation, has always particularly amazed me.

My uncle Oceanus, father of rivers, was given this task to perform.

Uranus had above all else a passion to create. Whether he brought the secret with him from infinite distances, or whether it was the intuition of a genius —in either case it was a gift of the Destinies—he possessed the Number of organic life. He made the species.

Everything that is verdant, flowers, swims, crawls, flies, walks or runs; everything that peoples the waters, cleaves the air, has roots in rock or humus; that eats, breathes, secretes; that sings, chirps, bleats, roars, calls, cries its desire, its fear or its joy; everything that produces egg, germ, seed or sperm; everything that divides and of which each half becomes a similar unit to the original; everything that is capable of containing within a minute portion of its substance its shape and characteristics so as to transmit them to a new, yet identical, being—these are his work.

I have said: the Number of life. And this, dear mortals, is where you start pondering. For this is what you have been trying to discover for so long!

Number is the Word but is not utterance; it is wave and light, though no one sees it; it is rhythm and music, though no one hears it. Its variations are limitless, and yet it is immutable. Each form of life is a particular reverberation of Number. Well, my sons, you will need to ponder for some time yet!

Uranus was prudent in his first experiments. Number must be handled with caution.

Certainly, the song of the amoeba might seem to be a little monotonous, and the piping of the first lichen a trifle thin. But from then on, what imaginative luxuriance, what speed of execution, what audacity of fugue, what inexhaustible richness of counterpoint, what generosity and amplitude in the symphony of the species!

Often, when making love to a mortal in a field, I forgot both her and what I had in hand in my astonishment at the varieties of grass beneath my eyes.

A tuft of grass—one says it so easily, and pays it so little attention! But look at it close to, and you will be fascinated, as I was, by the quantity of different plants composing that single tuft, by the variety of their stems, one square and hairy, another round and constructed of concentric tubes, another hollow, another solid, and yet another triangular. O Number, Number of infinite variety! You will admire the cleverness of the roots, the independence of the grains; and you will count the colors, all the shades of green which go to make up that single green you see from afar; and you will isolate each scent with delight.

Should you find yourself similarly distracted at such a moment, encourage your companion, for her part, to observe the flight of the sparrows or to meditate on the shape of the foliage sheltering you, and to take delight in them. And, afterwards, you will see how much more enjoyable love is!

For Uranus was proud of his labors, and justly so, and I, his heir and trustee, am proud on his behalf; we do not like you to pass through the rich gallery of his creation like dolts, seeing, understanding and appreciating nothing. But if you are prepared to forget yourself occasionally and gaze with concentration at *his* pine-cone, *his* pomegranate with its rosy heart, *his* iridescent dragonfly poised above a shimmering stream, *his* slow-worm asleep in the sun, coiled like the spirals of time between two stones, then happiness will be your reward. For you will have entered into communion with the vibrations of Number and the movement of the world.

Nor, for this purpose, do you need to be an intellectual with a well furnished mind, or the rich owner of many acres. A shepherd will often point these things out to you.

Vanished Species.
The Titans' Mad Ambition:
Their Activities;
Their Punishment.

Thus Uranus peopled the earth with everything that is in it. But there can be no great creation without much experimenting and frequent second thoughts. How many species there were of which nothing remains but their fossilized design embedded in the chalk, and how many others that still perpetuate themselves were but rough sketches for more finished products! How many wings were discarded as soon as invented, or welded to reptiles or attached to fish, before scales became feathers, and the wing reached perfection in the eagle and the dove!

Moreover, it so happened that the Titans became infected with a wild ambition and, instead of assisting their father, wished to rival him, believing themselves capable of surpassing his works.

Creation seemed to them so easy! Why did Uranus constantly pause over trifling details? Why spend centuries over the caterpillar's rings or the snail's horns, when you could make a cedar sprout in an instant from a mound of loose earth?

They were secretly encouraged by their mother the Earth.

But Uranus, though he had confided to his sons, when he set them to labor, certain variations of Number, had not revealed to them Number itself, nor all the arcana of its employment.

The Titans merely succeeded in producing gigantic, unbalanced animals, monsters with tiny brains that dragged their deformed and slimy bodies about with difficulty, hideous hydras with innumerable, inordinately long arms, furious dragons that tore nature apart with their claws, felled forests with a switch of their tails, and destroyed all life before them merely with their breath.

The Titans also let loose lunacy among plants. Damp mushrooms, so big they hid the sun, huge ferns, lianas of interminable length, dark top-heavy flowers, and vast leaves dripping sticky liquids threatened to stifle every living thing.

The Titans had acted from vanity and now could not arrest their creatures' growth. They had made use of the One-Eyed and the Hundred-Handed, but could not control them with the result that they behaved in a terrifying and disorderly way.

Uranus saw the danger and had to take violent action. He upset the climates, raised several mountain chains, dried up a number of seas, flooded various valleys, and by water, ice and fire annihilated the monsters his children had created. It is even possible that he shook the whole globe, slightly displacing its axis of rotation and somewhat altering the shape of its ellipse through space.

Then, when he had shamed the Titans with their absurd presumption, Uranus imprisoned them in the bowels of the Earth and forbade them ever to do it again. And he treated the Cyclopes and the Hecaton-cheires in the same way, for they were now of little use to him and had let themselves be led astray by their elders.

He made an exception only of Oceanus who, apart from experimenting with a few hydras, had stood rather aloof and had not really participated in his brothers' madness.

And Uranus also kept near him, to help him in his life-giving work, the nymphs and Titanides, in particular his daughter Memory, the most loving and faithful of them all, who was constantly at his side to keep a record of everything he did.

The Body of the Earth.
The Destinies.
The Language of the Gods.

You may perhaps be surprised and confused, mortals my sons, to hear me refer to the Earth sometimes as a being and sometimes as an object, sometimes as my grandfather's wife and sometimes as the scene of his labors.

To understand, you must think of your own bodies, of the flora that covers your entrails, of the ferments that develop in you by the myriad and there make their homes and found their families, of the bacilli which there wage war; you must think of all the microscopic things which inhabit your pores, tissues and fluids, and for which you are the unfathomable world. What do they know of you but the dark cavern of your pylorus or the tides of your stomachic ocean? And can they see or know what you are doing, when you penetrate your wives, or understand the cause or object of the tremors that shake you?

And so it is with you, who are tiny bacilli in the gigantic body of the universe, and can see but very little of it. For what you believe to be a brilliant light is merely a taper or a candle-end with which to explore gropingly your corner of darkness.

And so it is with us, yes, even with us, the gods, who are also subject to the Destinies.

For above all else are the Destinies, of whom you have not heard tell for a long time past. And yet no force and no life escapes them. Their decisions are rarely intelligible; their nature remains unknown to us. Without them, neither you nor I would exist. They give the first impulse, and set each course to its end; and though each of us is permitted to run that course well or ill, none may wander from it. Such are the Destinies, who are located around but far beyond the wheelings of our worlds, and they are so mysterious that one has said almost all there is to be said of them when one has so much as mentioned their name.

One may, on occasion, have some communication with them; but their faces always remain veiled.

There is one other point on which I must instruct you. In our language, we gods have three modulations for each word according to whether we wish to designate the principle of a thing, its manifestation or its absence. Bearing this in mind, strive to give my words their true meaning.

And now we can proceed.

Atlantis.
The Creation of Man.
The Golden Age.

So Uranus, husband of the Earth's principle, having restored order to the Earth's manifestation and imprisoned the Titans, the Hundred-Handed and the One-Eyed in the Earth's absence, took up residence on the continent of Atlantis.

The steps of his palace were of pure gold and its columns of rock-crystal; the walls were built of the most precious stones which, from amethyst to ruby, through sapphire and emerald, hymn the seven colors of light. And the roof was of diamond.

All around grew trees producing the finest essences,

and in them marvelous birds fluttered. The whole of Atlantis was like one huge garden carpeted with sweet-smelling flowers.

It was there, sitting on the golden steps, that Uranus created man, whom he considered his masterpiece. He meditated for a long time, and for a long time he sought the Number of the species he wished to be superior to all others.

If minds, as morose as they are ill-informed, have told you, dear mortals, that you are descended from apes, do not believe them. Apes were merely experiments, first drafts, rough sketches for man. To console them for their uncertain state, and to be rid of their squalling, my grandfather sent them to play in the beautiful trees in the garden. But they are not your ancestors.

You, who are generally so proud, often to excess, of your persons and your powers, should not be so humble as to consider yourselves perfected apes. Consider their agility. If you were super-apes your agility would be greater still than theirs. But Uranus endowed you with less so that you would be obliged to supplement it by the resources of your industry. For he wanted to confer on you some divine attribute, and you are not merely erect Quadrumana.

The Number of man is a particular Number, calculated for man, and for him alone. And when Uranus had discovered it, he at once made several variations of it, creating types of diverse colors, from amber to copper, from milk to ebony, and pygmies and giants, whom he scattered over the world. But of all these races, the most finished and the most perfect was that of the Atlantes, who lived in the Golden Age.

I did not know the Golden Age. It came to an end when the continent of Atlantis was overwhelmed and was already finished when I was born.

Thus, mortals, you should take note that your race is older than most of the gods.

I know, from my aunt Memory, that the men who lived in the gardens of Atlantis were two or three feet taller than you are. Your most splendid statues give but a feeble idea of their beauty of movement.

They knew no pain, poverty or care. Their houses had no doors for everything belonged to everyone. Since they were surrounded by inexhaustible abundance, war was unknown to them; and no one desired to possess more, nor had any reason to wish to be more powerful, than his neighbor. They were also immune to jealousy; men and women made love freely, in accordance with the varied and continually renewed incentives of the natural harmonies.

Animals showed no fear of man, for man had no inclination to kill. The Atlantes lived on grain, eggs and fruit, for they had been taught that they had a right to take the sources or reserves of life for their subsistence, but never to cut off a life that was already made manifest.

Though the Destinies, on entrusting Number to Uranus, had authorized him to create but only on condition that his creatures should be mortal, old-age and its accompanying ills were spared the men of the Golden Age. They rejoiced in their strength, their powers and their pleasures till the extreme evening of their lives; then, when their time, which was in the neighborhood of one thousand years, was running out, by a happy dispensation they felt weary of life, and entered peacefully into their last sleep.

The Atlantes used but few words, knowing that each word engenders active good or bad vibrations, and that their use must therefore be weighed. But they had complete communication of thought instead of that partial and invalid exchange which has, since then, and for want of anything better, constituted human language. They made use of the most marvelous cellular apparatus Uranus ever conceived, and which he had lodged behind their handsome brows. They could call and reply to each other silently over long distances, and see each other too, by selecting among all the waves which passed within their range. And, finally, they could hear the sublime music of the spheres spinning in the universe, and this kept them in a state of such dazzling happiness that it made of their lives one long festival.

The Last Works of Uranus.
The Selection of Species.
Domestic Animals.
The Sickle.
The Zodiac.

Uranus was deeply attached to his Atlantes; he was proud of them and rejoiced to see them in every way so perfectly happy.

He, himself, continued to create and create and create. He could not stop. Having made his masterpiece, he turned again to the works of his youth to correct and perfect them. He retouched the beetle, and redesigned the curves and flutings of the mollusk's shell with a purer line. If he was seen to be lost in thought on the threshold of his palace, gazing at some peculiar beauty of the sunset's coloring, next day a butterfly would be fluttering among the flowers, its wings sprinkled with a similar variety of sumptuous colors. A few grains of this powder happening to fall on the nail of his big toe gave Uranus his idea for the lady-bird's elytrum.

As some among you, dimly resembling him and vowed to the same exigencies, paint on canvas or hardboard, he painted on membrane, feather and fur;

he painted on the goldfish, he painted on the stork, he painted on the panther and the zebra. At one and the same time, he contrived the picture and its support. He sculpted in life. He was the supreme potter; and each work, as soon as it left his hands, had the gift of reproducing itself in thousands of copies, thus indefinitely preserving itself for the future.

Those who have tried to tell you that species evolve through battles among themselves, or through the struggle to survive in a harsh world, have looked at nature through clouded spectacles. If this were so, why should a thorn-tree and a smooth-trunked tree grow side by side in the same acre of ground? Why should their flowers have an unequal number of petals, and why should birds with wide beaks and birds with beaks as sharp as a needle, purple birds, speckled birds, black birds, birds with crests, hoods and pouches, some whistling and others chattering, live side by side among the same branches?

Whom does the frail tit, with its face painted like a sorcerer's mask, expect to frighten when it grasps a crumb in its tiny talons and assumes the air of a bird of prey? The mallard's green collar and the rosy patch on the flamingo's wing are calls to love, not weapons of war.

What defense, do you suppose, are the feathers of its tail to the peacock? Would not plain, thick, needle-pointed horns have been more use to the stag than the antlers he carries? If it was appetite that made the anteater's tongue to grow, how long do you think yours would be? And if the chameleon has so great a desire to escape notice, why does it not slip under the nearest stone like any lizard?

All this was the considered, deliberate work of a great artist, whose every imagining, every dream made sense. He wanted to exhaust every possibility, develop and combine every principle.

As gardener of the elements and of space, Uranus grafted; sometimes, for minor tasks, he confided his grafting-knife to his beloved Atlantes.

As mathematicians he used the results achieved. If your embryo has the shape of a tadpole and, for a while, the gills of a fish, it is because these were the initial and implicit calculations for operation man. And your genes contain much earlier and more secret figures.

It would seem that Uranus knew, at least in part, the decrees of the Destinies concerning his masterpiece; he was therefore careful to prepare the human race to confront the worst as well as to attain to the best.

In anticipation of the worst, he made to appear, by modifying existing species, the horse to carry man, the cow and the goat to feed him, and the dog to love him and guard him. In these, the original familiarity between human and animal was preserved; they have been both your servants and your companions through the Dark Ages, from which you can at moments see the way out, but from which you have not yet emerged.

It was also Uranus who forged the first sickle, under the eyes of man, in readiness for the day when man would be obliged to work. But in making this saving gift to his creature, did my grandfather know that he was also grinding the instrument of his own misfortune? The Destinies must be fulfilled even for the gods.

And, furthermore, since Uranus had knowledge of the rhythms that regulate the courses of the heavenly bodies—and, indeed, it is this fact which makes me think that he came from elsewhere and had been able to watch, in space, the system governing the worlds— he gave the Atlantes the calendar; and above all he taught them to read the great clock of the Zodiac on which are marked not only the months and the years of the earth, but also the eras of the universe, and which permits humans to discover the direction of their destinies and to conform to it.

Since the beginning of time you have wondered from where and from whom this clock of genius came into your hands. It came to you from Uranus, my sons, and from Atlantis. It is your most ancient heritage.

You were thus more or less armed. With a cow, a sickle and the Zodiac, one can do a great deal.

But Uranus had other and more ambitious dreams for you; he had inscribed them in the combinations of your Number; and he was already working to develop them, when the tragedy occurred.

Hatred of Gæa for Uranus.
Plot with the Titans.
Uranus Mutilated by
His Son Cronus.
The Children Born
of the Wound.
Aphrodite.
Uranus Retires into the Sky.

My grandmother Gæa, the Earth, had begun to hate her husband. She, who had once claimed to have begotten him, now wished only for his death. She accused him of being a bad father because he had imprisoned the Titans. She also reproached him with creating too much, and complained of being exhausted by his embraces. When women say they are weary of love, it is usually because they are weary of their lover and have their eyes already turned towards another. This other, in Gæa's case, was Pontus, the descendant of Chaos; and she proved it by abandoning herself to him as soon as she could.

Perhaps Uranus was wrong to be so faithful. He was the god of a single Earth. Had he been inconstant, he might have kept her more easily by making her anxious to hold him.

In fact, Gæa had nothing to reproach Uranus with other than his very nature and his celestial origin. When hatred becomes substituted for desire, all grounds of complaint are nothing but invention, and the only thing one resents in the other is the fact of his being what he is.

She had had too much of him; she was bored and wanted a change.

Mortals, my sons, always beware of our ancestor the Earth. She is irascible, quarrelsome and apt to be a termagant. She never liked Uranus's works. She has sly and sudden angers, which make her skin tremble, thereby destroying your finest cities as well as the temples you have dedicated to us. She engulfs you in her crevasses. During her days of impurity, she has volcanic boils which flow down in a havoc of fire. When she gives herself to Pontus, the Sea, tidal waves submerge your shores. She lets you labor with plough-share and spade, and then all of a sudden wickedly freezes your sowings or rots your harvest. Never trust her completely; and treat her with harshness and violence.

Having determined to be rid of Uranus, Gæa applied to the Titans who were imprisoned in her depths; she preached vengeance and rebellion to them, encouraging them to liberate themselves and free her at the same time. They all refused, since they did not dare leave the prison to which Uranus had consigned them, nor risk worse punishments if the plot were discovered; all, that is, except the youngest, Cronus, who was to be my father. He agreed to attempt the hideous crime, in return for a promise that he would be king of the world.

One night, with his mother's complicity, he escaped from his gaol in Tartarus. Having stolen the golden sickle forged for the Atlantes, Gæa gave it to him. Cronus lay in ambush.

As Uranus returned from flying over the continents, his mind full of the creative longings that precede sleep, and descended on the Mediterranean . . .

But have you pondered the contours of the Mediterranean, its shape, its recesses, its parturient breadth, and understood why it is the eternal source of great works and the mother of civilizations? The ovule, detaching itself from the Indian cluster, descends by the Persian valleys and the straits of the Near East. . . . Splendid; you have taken my point.

When Uranus descended on the Mediterranean at nightfall, his son Cronus, armed with the sickle, rose to his feet and at one blow severed his genitals.

The roar Uranus uttered that night filled the whole universe with terror.

Blood spurted from the wound and spread all around, on the waters and the earth. From it were born the Erinnyes, terrible divinities full of the fury of the father-god, and also the great Pan, and Silenus and the Fauns, the hosts of virile violence forevermore. Engendered by the primary forces flowing from the veins of Uranus, the monstrous race of giants arose, such as Alcyoneus, Ophion and Porphyrion, the red, stupid and brutal colossi who were to give me much trouble in the future. It was as if all the diverse energies composing the blood of the founder had divided and dispersed so as to become separately incarnate.

One drop fell on a sleeping horse. He woke up the first centaur, which is clear evidence of the dreams Uranus was cherishing at the time of his misfortune.

Do not think that the milky, seminal foam that escaped from the wound was lost. Projected afar, it frothed upon the sea by Cyprus; and there, at the next dawn, Aphrodite rose from the waves; with her amber arms, her slender fingers and her exquisite breasts, she is the most beautiful, apparently the most desirable, and certainly the most desired of goddesses. But Aphrodite is cruel and cold, even in her passions; she is inhabited by nothing but self-love and throbs only to the suffering one reaps from loving her. Branded by her father's sorrow as if by a curse, she pursues, unwearied and unwearingly, ever hopeful and ever disappointed, a happiness to which she ceaselessly approaches but to which she can never attain.

When Uranus realized who had done this thing to him, he told Cronus in a terrible voice that he would suffer a similar fate and that he, too, would be dethroned by one of his sons. This prophecy was the last speech he uttered for he then withdrew into the farther distances of the sky, his origin, and there lies in repose, beyond the reach of gravitation, detached, immortal, and forever mute.

If you wish to know why Uranus, the demiurge, on being mutilated, abandoned the calculations, drafts and grafts on which he was engaged, renounced the perfecting of his work, even the superintending of

it, and left life more or less to itself, ask my son
Hermes, who invented your language for you and
formed gene, genital and genius from a single root.

Mortals, who now share with us the power of moving through the air—I was wrong at the beginning to
deny you all innovation; we shall speak of this again
—when you happen to fly over the island of Corfu,
observing its shape and how the vegetation is ordered
there, you will understand why it was originally
known by the name of Corcyra, which in the common speech means the Phallus. We, both gods and
men of the Mediterranean, make irreverent jokes of
the kind. . . .

It is also said that when Cronus threw away the
tragic sickle, it fell into the sea, that the handle became Cape Drepanum, and that the sublime curve of
the Gulf of Nauplia owes its beauty to the divine
particles with which the golden blade was charged,
that blade one sees so bright and huge on summer
evenings when the sun bathes it in his last fires.

The Reign of Cronus.
The Titans Freed.
The Loves of the Earth
& Pontus.
The Baneful Divinities.
The End of
the Golden Age.

As soon as my father Cronus became master of the world, he freed his brothers. He took his sister Rhea, of the beautiful hair, for wife. And the other Titans married other Titanides or nymphs. There were born during his reign a quantity of minor gods, children and grandchildren, cousins and parents combined.

Gæa, the Earth, in the transports of her new passion, was continually offering herself to Pontus's embraces. And Night, another daughter of ancestor Chaos, considered it permissible to find delight in the arms of her brother Erebus, god of the Infernal Regions.

Eros presided impartially over all these unions. His duty was to impel forces towards each other, not to be concerned about the consequences. Moreover, our world is not the only one with which he has to deal, and the embraces of Earth are far from being his only care.

From these immoderate and disorderly copulations, there resulted, to mention only a few, the Gorgons and the sad Medusa, the two Harpies and pitiless Nemesis, as well as Lies, Discord, Hunger, Pain, Age, Murder, Anarchy and Disaster.

One cannot suddenly turn oneself into a king; ambition to rule is no justification for possessing power. My father's reign was wholly detestable. Was not one of the versions of his name Chronos, Time the Destroyer?

The Golden Age was being torn to shreds.

Though Oceanus, and his beautiful wife Tethys, remained somewhat aloof from these follies, and viewed his mother's behavior with the Sea with a contemptuous eye, though my dear aunt Memory, who was devoted to the memory of her father, refused to marry, reserving herself, as we shall see, for a later love, and though my sister Themis the Law maintained a similar attitude, the other Titans began once again to behave with the utmost stupidity. In reaction to their long imprisonment, they overran Atlantis, sacked it and maltreated the Atlantes, who, in despair at having lost their king, were beginning to feel fatigue, diminish in stature, and fear death.

The One-Eyed and the Hundred-Handed had also been freed, for Cronus, in his crafty way, thought he could make use of them to his greater glory. But unable to control them, instead of getting useful work out of them, he obtained nothing but immeasurable havoc. Arges, the cyclopeian lightning-bearer, set many a forest alight because he was asked for a fire of twigs!

This is the kind of thing that often happens both with gods and men of the second generation. Impatient to rob their father of his authority, they believe themselves capable of improving on his work but succeed only in spoiling it.

Cronus was never happy. Encouraged by his mother, he had been jealous of Uranus since his earliest childhood. But having emasculated and supplanted him, he achieved no greater peace. He was morose, malevolent and always anxious. He wished to justify his crime by proving, both to others and himself, that he was superior to the founder, or at least his equal. He never succeeded. Can Space and Time be one?

Impressed by the appearance of the centaur, he had the idea, which he believed to be one of genius, of combining the principles of man with certain animal principles so as to obtain stronger and more powerful beings. It would appear that he succeeded in producing a man-lion, a man-bull and a man-ram, of which the Atlantes, who later came to Egypt and Assyria, retained the memory. But my aunt Memory asserts that Cronus lied and, rather than admit his failures, disguised some of the giants in animals' masks. In any case, none of his supposed creatures had the power of reproducing itself.

The fact was that Cronus had not understood Uranus's intentions with regard to the centaur. It was not a question of grafting man onto animals, but of graft-

33

ing him onto the stars in accordance with the different hours or eras of the Zodiac. Uranus was considering a race of celestial men. And the Atlantes, who had understood this, kept silence.

Perhaps one day, if the Destinies have so decided, man, at the highest point of the curve, will rise among the constellations and fulfill the demiurge's dream.

Cronus in Search
of Number.
The Disappearance
of Atlantis.
The First Flood.
Dispersal of the Atlantes.

Oh Cronus, too Earth-bound, too clumsy, and too bitter! He succeeded in working only lead and base metals.

Sometimes, looking up at the sky, he cried angrily: "Father, father, how did you do it? Where have you hidden Number?"

But Uranus never answered him.

Furious with impotent rage, Cronus took it into his head that Number was hidden somewhere in his father's palace. Summoning the Hecatoncheires, he made them take up the golden flagstones, and pull down the emerald and opal walls. The Titans and Cyclopes assisted them. The terrified Atlantes began to retreat to the far end of their garden.

If Number was not in the foundations, it must clearly be in the roof. In order to find what Cronus was seeking, it might have been better to consider the shape of the roof rather than to destroy it. But it was not to be. The Hundred-Handed tore the diamond pyramid to pieces, reducing each stone to brilliants, and each brilliant to dust. The palace had ceased to exist, and Number had not been found.

They brought Cronus the extreme point of the roof, the molecule, lighter than dew, with which the building had once touched the sky. And Cronus ordered the lightning-bearing Cyclopes to open this molecule.

Oh unfortunate father! Did you not know that in Uranus's work the infinitely large is contained in the infinitely small, and that if you destroy one speck of the infinite, the whole collapses?

A huge flower of fire rose from the Earth, wine-dark at the center, livid at the edges, and spread monstrously. Everything became covered with a dense cloud, a vapor of rock, metal and life. The Earth disappeared from the sight of the other heavenly bodies and, for a moment, Chaos thought his daughter was dead.

Atlantis had disappeared.

Several neighboring seas evaporated, among them the great African sea, to fall again elsewhere in heavy, continuous, flooding rain that lasted for days and days. You could no longer see the fields, the tops of the trees, the crests of the hills. The water rose and rose.

The Earth, as if she still wished to be revenged on Uranus, allowed herself, beneath his very eyes, to be embraced and covered by Pontus. Never had they abandoned themselves to their pernicious gambols with such wanton shamelessness. The sea had taken the place of the sky.

This was the first Flood.

Cronus gazed into the abyss, in which were piled the huge ruins of the shattered continent, as if it were a personal affront! The depths of Tartarus were visible through the fissures. But do you think my father grasped the extent of his folly, presumption and error? Do you think he realized that the principle of things must never be used except for the manifestation of things, or, in other and more human terms, that no energy must ever be released except for the purpose of construction or production, for otherwise it becomes annihilation and merely the absence of things?

My father turned his rancor upon the One-Eyed and the Hundred-Handed, whom he accused of incompetence and treason. He cast them back into the abysmal prison to which Uranus, in his wisdom, had previously consigned them. Poor giants, poor god-forces at the disposal of god-thoughts, were they responsible for the wicked use that had been made of them?

These, more or less, are my aunt Memory's recollections of the disaster. She was indeed so moved that her eyes were for a moment blinded by tears. Usually so clear and precise, she does not much like talking of the tragedy; her account of it is reticent, and as if deliberately obscure and confused. It is as if she fears a similar tragedy may happen again one day.

My uncle Oceanus, cleverly draining away all the waters that had fallen back on the Earth, used them to cover the ruins of Atlantis, thus concealing his brother's misdeeds, and allowing Uranus's works to perpetuate themselves.

Those of the Atlantes who lived on the perimeter of the great garden, or had taken refuge there, and had thus escaped, dispersed to one side or the other of the abyss, some towards the Andes and even farther, some to the hollow of the gulf formed by Brittany and Iberia, some towards Etruria, some towards the river Nile and its sources, some towards the Tigris, and some towards the five rivers of India and the Tibetan plateau. They mingled with the other variously colored human races my grandfather had created. But the clouds which fell from the flower of fire had started ailments which became concentrated in their genes, and from which you still suffer. The length of their lifetimes was reduced to a tenth of what it had previously been; their stature was diminished and became as yours is now. And the explosion had affected their ears and had deprived them forever of listening to the music of the spheres.

Wherever they went, they erected obelisks to Uranus; these were sometimes humble and sometimes of enormous size, sometimes rough-hewn and sometimes perfectly shaped, according to the means at their disposal; but they all expressed to him their sorrow at his mutilation, and preserved the image of that of which he had been deprived; and they also built pyramids in memory of his palace.

And they were able to build these tall, massive and expert works, with nothing but stones to hand, because they had retained the science Uranus had taught them in the happy days of Atlantis; and, similarly, wherever they went, they reproduced the great celestial clock, the Zodiac with its twelve marvels.

It was at about this time I was born.

THE SECOND EPOCH

Crete
Was My Cradle

Cronus and His Children.
The Essence of Life.
The Despair of Rhea.
The Subterfuge.
The Birth of Zeus.

D espite what is generally believed, my early life was appalling. My father ate his children.

Mortals, my sons, you who appear only to disappear, who are inexorably taken back by the force that created you, who are condemned from your first cry, you for whom all the happiness of living, planning, acting, and all the charms of loving are constantly frustrated by the haunting obsession of that moment when the jaws of Time will close on you, this is what brings us closer together and helps us to understand each other.

You will therefore not be surprised that I never loved my father and have always judged him without indulgence or affection.

He always remembered Uranus's prophecy and, wise from the experience of his own crime, distrusted any prison other than his own entrails for the incarceration of offspring destined to dethrone him.

As soon as my mother had given birth, and the child scarcely at her knees, Cronus would seize the rosy newly born and devour it.

Thus my five brothers and sisters, Hades, Poseidon, Hestia, Demeter and Hera were swallowed up without ever having seen the world.

In that case, you will ask, why did Cronus continue to pleasure his wife? Would he not have been both wiser and less cruel to restrain his transports and retain his seed?

Mortals, dear mortals, are you really in a position to ask such a question? How many among you, both men and women, while unable to resist the solicitations of desire, reject its fruits even before they appear, as if you saw in them a curse or a limitation placed on your own destiny? These, to some extent, resemble the saturnine Cronus.

Everything appertaining to the essence of life is naturally tragic, since nothing is born into the universe except by the attraction of two forces, each avid for the other, which consume themselves by their junction to create a third in which they destroy themselves. Yet at the same time there is no true happiness or zest for life except for and in this conflagration. Number and the Destinies are made manifest and contained in it.

And Cronus, like you, aspired to the repeated joys of this conflagration while desiring to escape the calamity of being consumed.

Your most inspired sages have said: "He who accepts Destinies is guided; he who rejects them is forcibly led."

My mother Rhea, of the beautiful hair, lived in panic through the eras. Always pregnant, always mourning her previous child, always fearful for the child to be born, she now submitted to her brother's embraces with anguish and horror. And it was little consolation to her to be looked on as the queen of the world.

While she was carrying me, she went to seek the advice of my grandmother the Earth, who saw in her daughter's complaints the same grievances she had nourished against her own husband.

I must tell you that Gæa had considerably altered her attitude towards Cronus since he had been reigning; she reproached him with the bad government of the empire, to which she had raised him, and thought him ungrateful for not paying her proper and constant homage for what he owed her. O you tyrannical mothers, who through your children love only yourselves, who are prepared to do anything, however criminal, to assure your own triumph through them, and who seek only to injure them as soon as they escape from your authority! What a breed of Agrippinas you are!

I owe my life to this hatred of mother for son.

The subterfuge the Earth suggested to her daughter Rhea may not seem particularly subtle; its audacity lay in imagining that so absurd a proceeding had any chance of success.

The night my mother was due to be brought to bed, she went secretly to Crete and bore me in a cave. Then, in the morning, she took a large stone from the mountain, wrapped it in swaddling clothes, and, returning to her husband, handed it to him while pretending to disconsolate resignation. My father, distracted by his failures, was once again pondering his anger against the Cyclopes; he took the disguised stone and swallowed it at a single gulp.

So as to conceal me from Cronus, should his suspicions ever be aroused, my mother had chosen to have me born in human form, which most closely approaches the nature of the gods and best permits the developing of their gifts. From a distance, I might have been taken for any human child.

It was thus I was saved. The Destinies could now be fulfilled.

Later, when I became a god revealed, I never forgot my first incarnation and was to remain always influenced by it.

As king of the gods, and able to manifest myself in any guise I chose, it was yours I most readily assumed to accomplish my tasks, suffer my sorrows, and experience my joys. I am the god of mankind; do not forget it.

Crete.
Mount Iouktas.
The Cave of Psychro.

It had always been foreseen that I would be born in Crete. Since the beginning of the ages, my image had been there, dominating the island and visible from ten leagues away. The sailors will point it out to you, as it rises above the prow, if you come from the north to land at Heraklion; and you will also see it if you land on the southern shore and take the road which rises towards Akarnes. Never, either of god or man, has a bigger effigy been made than this, which was molded on my future. It is a mountain and its name is Iouktas.

My body does not appear; it has not been released from the masses of rock and time. My head alone emerges, standing out against the sky, a reclining profile that looks as if it were asleep. My eye is closed. My nose is not curved and melancholy, but sensual and rounded at the tip; it points towards the skies. My elaborate, handsome beard spreads out below my lip and slopes gently down towards the next mountain.

Uranus had commissioned the work from the Hundred-Handed, so that he might gaze on the face of his future grandson, the master of the gods to be, and that it might one day be recognized by men. That is why, since I made myself manifest, this mountain is also called the Head of Zeus.

I like Crete, and have always been grateful to it. Its golden earth, covered with a garment of wild herbs and for long months crushed by the heat, takes on the colors of a beautiful red-haired woman's body lying in the sun.

I endowed it, in the time of the Bull, with a hundred flourishing towns; I made the way of knowledge pass across it; I made its kings powerful in fabulous palaces, and gave its artists the genius to create designs and forms that remain an unfailing source of meditation. It has been the link between your memories and your hopes. I took the inventive Daedalus there, that excellent architect, who was at once a bronze-founder, a sculptor and an applied engineer. It was there he made wings for himself and his son Icarus. It was in my native Crete that your race began to soar again.

The cave in which I was born lies on the convex heights of Mount Dicte, above the village of Psychro. Gods can land there easily enough, but man can reach it only with difficulty by paths, scarcely visible in the brush, on which mules pick up stones in their hooves. In the summer there is a scent of wild herbs, and the air is always quivering a little like a shaken veil.

Here was my first sanctuary; though it has but few pilgrims now.

The cave is covered with a damp secretion. The rock weeps time away in long stalactites, giant calcareous water-clocks, which form the natural columns of this my first temple. A bull's-eye of light casts a diffused ray over the greenish vault. You have to go down and down, two hundred feet into the night of the Earth.

He, who has slithered over these blocks of stone, which were the eyrie of my birth, a quivering wax flame in his hand, will on emerging walk through the world with a firmer step.

He, who has entered these shadows, will, on returning from them, be aware of greater clarities.

He, who has entered that utter silence, will ever afterwards be able to hear my voice amid the tumult.

He, who had bathed his face in the dark, seminal waters that fill the bottom of the cave, will be re-born and become aware of a new and righteous longing to be guided along a righteous path.

And if he is really my son, a descendant of my race, then, when he returns to the light of day, the nymph Amaltheia will appear to him, take him by the hand, and place a kiss on his lips.

The Nymph Amaltheia.
The Goat.
The Curetes.
The Nymph Melissa.

Almost naked, her hair short and her feet bare, Amaltheia danced over the mountain at dawn on the first morning of my life. She heard my cries and, guided by them, found me in the cave. It was she who fed me.

Not she herself, the dear girl, as has been said. She was an adolescent nymph who had never borne a child, and what milk could she have drawn from her little rosy breasts? She went to fetch her goat from the village of Psychro and led it by the horn to the cave. Later, when I began to talk, I called both the nymph and the goat by the same name, believing there was only one word for the benefits I received. And the confusion was perpetuated. This took place in one of the times of Capricorn.

The next night, my mother Rhea returned secretly. She was continually looking over her shoulder, fearing that Cronus was in pursuit of her. She found me fed and asleep, a drop of milk at the corner of my mouth. A moonbeam—the moon was then in its first quarter—was shining through the bull's-eye. The goat was asleep in a corner of the cave; and Amaltheia, the nymph, was sitting watching over me.

On seeing the guardian the Destinies had sent me, my mother confided her secret to her in a low voice, told her all about me, and gave her many instructions and much advice. Then, weeping, she enveloped herself in the first passing cloud and left.

Amaltheia watched over me day and night. She was youth devoted to childhood, discovering in herself a desire to protect and marveling at the little god asleep in the chubby, fragile infant's body.

My eyes opened on the long, muscular, almost boyish thighs of the mountain nymph. And it may be the memory of Amaltheia's body, offered so naïvely to my first glances, that has made me love flaxen-haired women so much. But I have also loved many others.

Amaltheia was afraid that my horrible father would suddenly discover my existence. She used ingenuous tricks, and, when she had to leave me for a while, she hung me from a tree by a system of thongs, so that Cronus, if he were searching for me, would be unable to find me on earth, sea, or in the sky.

The secondary gods of nature have private understandings among themselves. Amaltheia appealed to her cousins the Curetes, young demons descended from Oceanus who had been turned out of Euboea because they were too noisy. Having continued their racket in various islands, they had come to live in Crete, near Cnossos. Amaltheia asked them to drown my wails, which certainly proved by their violence that I was no ordinary child. Whenever I began to cry, the Curetes set about dancing, clattering their spears and their big bronze shields, which had been given them by their mother Combe, daughter of the river-god Asopus. And this they did throughout the time I was teething.

Amaltheia had a sister, Melissa, the bee-nymph. She knew how to care for bees, speak to them, take them, and lead them to the most scented flowers. Melissa never moved without her accompanying bees; her passing was encompassed by a golden flight. She placed a swarm at the entrance to the cave, and the honey which flowed from the pressed combs was my second food.

I did not at first understand the restrictions with which Amaltheia surrounded me when I began to walk. I was not to go too far from the cave; I was not to go near the ravines. If the sun was too strong, I had to stay in the shade of the trees; if a threatening cloud appeared, I had to go in. On days of storm or mist, Amaltheia stood in the shelter of the rock and gazed anxiously out at the curtain of the rain or the veils of the mist.

Dear Amaltheia! She did not know that the wicked are easily deceived by the confidence they have in their own cruelty. The stone he carried in his stomach, mingled with my brothers and sisters, gave Cronus assurance.

The Horn of Plenty &
the Pleasure of Giving.
King Melisseus.
The First Sacrifices.

Having been born in human shape, my growth
followed the human rhythm. Nevertheless, I was already displaying unusual powers. One day, when I
was playing with the goat, one of its horns, which
were long and helical as are those of the island goats,
came away in my hand. I smilingly gave the horn,
which I had innocently broken off, to Amaltheia. It
was the first present I made her. I did not understand
why the nymph was so moved by the gift of the horn,
covered it with kisses, and pressed it to her breast. But
at the sight of her pleasure, I discovered the divine
joy of giving.

Amaltheia used the hollow horn when she went to
gather fruit from the wild trees or berries from the
bushes. When carrying it, she never came back empty-
handed. On her return, she shook the horn and the
fruits fell in a heap on the grass. What happy meals we
made in the mouth of the cave off these sweet or bitter
fruits on hot days!

The horn of plenty, of which you dream so often,

is still in Amaltheia's possession. The nymph has merely to turn it up and shake it and all the fruits of happiness spill out. But Amaltheia dispenses them only to those she recognizes as my sons by some spontaneous gift to her, made without thought of return, exchange, or even because it is customary.

Amaltheia was a king's daughter. She told me this when I was seven years old, explaining to me at the same time what a king was. Yes, indeed, life is full of these surprises! The race of kings does not always go crowned, but may sometimes be concealed beneath a short peasant's smock. It is by their heart and their bearing that princes must be judged, rather than by their attire, if one does not wish to make too many mistakes.

Amaltheia's father was called Melisseus and reigned over Crete at that time. His wife was descended from my grandfather Uranus, by the first generation of nymphs. Because of this, though Melisseus's sons were mortal, his daughters were not. Amaltheia and her sister Melissa had chosen the life of the fields in preference to the obligations of the palace, and the wise king had not opposed them. He was to congratulate himself later on, when he learned of the task to which they had devoted their freedom.

Melisseus, moreover, was the first man to think of making sacrifices to the gods, and of reducing to smoke some heads of his cattle and some portion of his goods, which was the only way of sending his offerings to us in the sky. This is perhaps the place to remind you, mortals, that to sacrifice does not necessarily mean to kill, as you have come to believe. To sacrifice means to deduct part of what one has in thanksgiving for having it, to subtract part of what one possesses, to deprive oneself of it and to give it voluntarily, in gratitude for all that one has been vouchsafed.

For a long time the sages, whom the very exercise of their wisdom prevented from possessing anything, and the poor whom the Destinies had deprived of all means of acquiring it, were fed on the flesh of the sheep and oxen that were sacrificed to the gods. And neither the sage nor the poor man felt humiliated by these gifts, any more than the king derived a sense of pride from them, since the smoke from these spits was intended for us. These were not meals of charity, but of universal gratitude, in which the prince and the priest, the rich and the poor, joined in celebrating the divine benefactions.

If the first sacrifices were of cattle, it was because Melisseus was a pastoral king and his wealth grazed the grass of the fields. You can nevertheless follow his example without being the owner of flocks and herds. Piety does not reside in the sheep; but in the act of sacrificing and sharing.

It was in this way that King Melisseus showed his greatness. Let his name escape oblivion and be honored.

Adolescence.
My Anxieties &
First Desires.

Vhen she judged my understanding sufficiently developed, Amaltheia revealed to me who I
was, to what future I was destined, and against what
perils I must be forearmed. Then began the years of
waiting, those anxious years between the end of childhood and the beginning of adolescence.

I knew myself to be a god, but I had not the powers
of a god. I relieved my sterile impatience by twisting
trees and breaking stones; and also by dreaming. I
spent interminable hours sitting on the mountain, my
arms clasped round my knees, watching the sea gleam-
ing in the distance, and imagining the day when I
should at last be able to prove to the world that I was
Zeus—should that day ever come. . . .

Meanwhile, the menace of my father filled me with
anxiety.

To be devoured in the unconsciousness of infancy
was one thing; but the prospect of dying when one
was already formed, aware, and full of vigor, hopes
and desires, was appalling. The fear of returning to
non-existence is never so lively and obsessive than at
this age of transition, when one is conscious of one's

latent powers but has not yet got them fully at command.

The nights became a torture to me. The fear which harassed me held me exhausted on the brink of sleep. Or I would wake suddenly, gasping and shattered.

Amaltheia watched me suffer and suffered herself from being unable to help me.

You forgetful adults, never say that adolescence is a wonderful time. And if yours seems to you to have been so, it is because you have done very little in your maturity.

Everything about my destiny seemed to me unjust. I did not know my mother; so as not to endanger me, or endanger herself, she had never returned. Nature's foundling, I felt frustrated and lonely. I had no friends, could have none, and wished for none. The island seemed to me a prison and I longed to get away from it.

At one time, I began to hate Amaltheia. Her advice, her counsel, her care for me, her efforts to cheer me and even her devotion had all become odious to me.

Then, a little later, I began to desire her.

Our ages were beginning to approach each other. She was still my elder, but by only a few years.

It began one afternoon when she was warming thyme leaves in the palms of her hands and making me smell them. I suddenly noticed, as I had never done before, the sweet curve of her forehead, her eyelashes fluttering rapidly over her blue eyes, her tenderly shaped mouth, half sulky, half sensual, the delicate line of her neck on which the light danced as if it were caught in the net of the soft golden down.

55

It seemed to me that I had never till that moment either looked at or known Amaltheia. I felt a strange thrill run through me stirring my heart with a force that was both happy and disquieting.

What was ancestor Eros doing in Crete at that moment? Where was he hidden? In the sprigs of thyme, in the furtive, rhythmic gliding of a snake, or simply in the arrows of the light?

Amaltheia was looking at me too, and seemed surprised at what she saw. Her eyes moved slowly from mine down to my chest, which was rising and falling with my quickening breath, moved down again, and she suddenly blushed. She got quickly to her feet and shook her hands as if to get rid of the scent; then, picking up the horn of plenty, she ran off towards the bushes to pick fruit of which we had no need.

And, thereafter, whenever she saw a similar look in my eyes or the signs of desire in me, she invented some reason to leave me.

If I merely began to say something by speaking her name in a rather hoarse voice, she would quickly place her hand over my mouth, as if I were interrupting her train of thought about some important matter.

In the evenings, she would occupy my mind by talking to me of my future duties as a god.

At one time, I thought she was beloved by a faun or by some other natural male divinity. I spied on her, but could discover nothing.

Our first ardors surprise us, and to be made manifest they need encouragement. Mine received none, and in the end I persuaded myself that Amaltheia was a nymph who was a stranger to love, and that what I wanted from her was either incomprehensible or displeasing to her.

There followed strange months during which each involuntary contact was followed by a hasty retreat, and every word I said had a double meaning that Amaltheia pretended not to understand.

To use up the forces that were consuming us, we made long, wild expeditions across the island. I was a strong young god, but already carried a certain weight. Great speed was never my forte. The nymph easily kept pace with me and sometimes outstripped me. I could beat her only over distance.

We discarded some of our former prudence, and if Cronus did not see us as we chased each other over the hills, or collapsed, breathless and laughing, on the grass, it was because his gaze was really turned away from men and he feared nothing that could appear in their shape.

We used to go down to the shore, to the sandy beaches or where soft pebbles rolled beneath the foot like stone eggs, and throw ourselves into a sea that was as warm as our bodies.

The sun set over carved and brazen promontories.

Oh Amaltheia, how beautiful you were, lying on your back on the waters, your brow crowned with gold, your thighs veiled by the blue, silky translucence, and your gently moving feet bathed in stardust!

Idiot that I was, I grew angry and took offense at the thought that she preferred the elements to me. I was jealous, and would shout to her to come out.

57

If she never succumbed during these days, it was proof rather of her courage than of my perspicacity.

And so, as you can see, my amorous history, of which so much has been said, and indeed with some justification, began with a disappointment. But how salutary that disappointment was!

The adolescent is too inclined to look on love as an exploit and to become accustomed all too quickly to be content with it as such. Indulged too soon, it diverts from work and power, and becomes their substitute instead of being their attribute and their recompense.

Amaltheia knew the decrees of the Destinies concerning me. She respected the god she had brought up. Had she yielded to my desires, by yielding to her own, I would have remained riveted to my human shape and the jaws of Time would have closed on me.

My sons, do not go to the cave of Psychro too young. When more mature, you will derive greater instruction from it.

Forever adolescent, the nymph Amaltheia still wanders about that neighborhood. Should she lead you over the rocks or mold her body to yours on the beach, do not think too lightly of her, nor too highly of yourself, but rather recognize the divine gift that is being made you by proxy. For she is eternally seeking me in your arms.

The Death of the Goat.
The Making of Aegis.
Departure from Crete.

And the kind goat that had fed me died, at an age to which ordinary goats never attained. We were sad about it, Amaltheia even more than I, for she recognized in this a sign of approaching changes.

On the clock of the eras, which turns in the opposite direction to the years of the Earth, Capricorn yields his reign to Saggitarius, which is the time of Battles.

The nymph Amaltheia cut up the goat Amaltheia with a sharp stone.

It was a painful and repugnant task; but Amaltheia said it must be done. Refusing my help, she detached the skin, went to dip it in a particular spring, rubbed it with selected herbs, and put it out to dry in a certain place on the mountain where the winds from the four horizons met. Then she spread the skin on two crossed sticks, cut from strong and supple bushes, and left it there for seven nights to grow soft in the dew and for seven days to grow hard in the sun.

On the morning of the eighth day, her eyes bright with both tears and pride, Amaltheia gave me the goat's-skin shield she had made for me.

It was Aegis.

As soon as I had taken it, with my left hand clasping the cross formed by the sticks, I felt myself swell and grow extraordinarily taller, broader, greater and more powerful, as those who are part of me sometimes do in dreams, but only in dreams. I had been reunited with my divine nature. My feet were touching the roots of the world; my brow reached to the highest realms of space. I could see before me all the isles of Greece rising out of the sea, the path prepared for the progress of gods and civilizations.

I saw Amaltheia standing near the cave, holding the horn of plenty in her hand. She was looking up, searching everywhere for me, but could already see me no longer.

I set out, guided by that sense of necessary action which both gods and migratory birds possess. With a few strides, I descended Cape Sidero and left Crete, the country of my childhood, touched down on Casos and Carpathos, and again on Rhodes above the charming Bay of Lindos, and following the great path of the islands I continued my journey northwards.

THE THIRD EPOCH

The Loves
That Form Youth

Metis the Prudent.
Her Counsel.
The Gift of the Drug.

The first divinity I met was sitting on an island, and looked so much a part of it against the setting sun that I nearly went by without seeing her. One of her legs was outstretched to the sea; and the waves were caressing her foot. Her other leg was bent and her arm was resting on it. She was leaning against a rampart of hills and her dark hair might have been taken for a pine wood. She had only to glance over the top of the island to watch the horizon in every direction.

I told her my name. She gazed at me for a long while from her almond eyes, which were as dark as her hair. Her skin was brown and her breasts rather heavy. She asked me many questions, listening to my voice and considering my replies, before telling me she was my cousin Metis, or Prudence if you prefer it, the daughter of Oceanus and Tethys, and that she was there to await my coming.

I told her I was setting off to conquer the world and besought her to give me help and counsel. She ordered me to say no more about it till nightfall.

To pass the time, I asked her if she had children.

She replied: "I am Prudence."

I also asked her, since in the measure of the age of the gods she was not quite thirty, if she desired a husband. She made the same answer and added: "I have refused several."

Then, as on sitting down I had left Aegis some little distance off, she said: "Keep it beside you."

When dusk had completely fallen, Metis questioned me on how I proposed to set about dethroning my father. She realized, and made me realize, that though I entertained many ambitions for the future, after the victory had been won, I had no plan for the battle itself.

"Daring and valor will be of no use to you unless you have planned your action. However strong one may be, let me tell you that one cannot win a war without allies. And the best you could have are in your enemy's stomach."

She said all this in a very low voice, continuing the while to agitate the sea with the tips of her toes, thereby drowning our murmured conversation in the noise of the waves.

She put her hand into a cleft in the rock and drew out of it a big shell full of a dark liquid, no doubt distilled from fish or seaweed.

"Take this drug," Metis said, "and make Cronus swallow it so that he vomits out your brothers. Hasten, and act before morning."

I got to my feet and hesitated a moment as to which direction to take. Metis licked her finger, as sailors have done ever since, to determine the direction of the breeze.

"Conceal your approach," my cousin added, "by going upwind."

Cronus Obliged to
Regurgitate His Children.
His Fury.

My father was asleep among thick clouds, lying extended under the circle of the Zodiac, but facing the wrong way, his knees towards the Bull, and his head on the level of the Scorpion. He was not at all horrible or monstrous, as I had always imagined him to be. Indeed, he was even handsome; and for a moment I was nonplussed.

I, who am a fair, rosy-skinned god, and was already aware that I was destined to a certain stoutness, began to envy his wiry slenderness, his mysterious brow, his arched and haughty nose, his long, dark, fine, commanding hands, his muscular chest and smooth belly. The seductions of appearance are dangerous, and one is in danger of weakening at the sight of one's rival sleeping.

65

I began to think, wondering if I could not come to an understanding with my father and share the kingdom with him.

But he began dreaming and, as if aware of my hidden presence, started opening and closing his jaws in his dream.

I then hesitated no longer and, when he opened his lips again, I took advantage of it to pour the emetic Prudence had given me down his throat.

The world quaked six times that morning as if another Atlantis were being destroyed. Cronus first vomited the stone which had been substituted for me; and it stuck in the Earth at the foot of Parnassus. It was then he realized how he had been duped; but his fury merely served to increase his spasms. Bent down towards the Earth, and each time a prey to harrowing agonies, he brought up my brothers and sisters one after the other. And since they were immortal and their principle had developed during their confinement in the dark, they attained their full height and adult strength immediately on being restored to the light of day.

Your history, mortals, furnishes similar examples. Liberty has never died from being imprisoned.

Cronus spent all day hurrying about the globe, wild with rage and also with anxiety, trying to find his wife so as to punish her for having deceived him, his children who had escaped him so as to annihilate them, and in particular that son, myself, who he knew was a menace to his reign. But all nature abetted us.

My grandmother Gæa gave asylum to my mother

and my sisters among her mountains. My brother Hades hid in an abyss; and my other brother, Poseidon, found refuge with our uncle Oceanus. As for me, the most endangered, I returned to Metis on her rock. She covered me with her shadow. Cronus once passed so close to us that I was very afraid of being discovered. But Metis pointed in the direction of the sun, and this dazzled him. He continued his furious course, sinking a few islands beneath his heel and causing a few others to spring up.

Then propitious night fell over us again.

Second Night with Metis.
Birth of Athena.

Spending thus a second night side by side, we were assailed by a great desire to unite. Prudent though she may be, Metis has nevertheless a feminine nature. She was attached to me because of the help she had given me; and my first exploit, which had been accomplished on her advice, inspired her with as much desire to become my first mistress as it did me to become her first lover.

Nevertheless, her instinct was to escape both from herself and from me. She was so difficult, and had

67

waited so long to make love! She hid herself in the fringes of the sea, in the sand of the shore, in the whisper of the breeze; but I thwarted all these tricks. When in love, you find love everywhere and in everything. Seeing the sort of god I was, and that I also instantly transformed myself so as to be with her, Metis yielded, delighted to accept defeat.

But she did not discard her nature all at once, for she said: "Consider what you are doing. You will have a child by me. I must help you and not be jealous of you, assist you and not supplant you. You must have a daughter. Think of the daughter you are about to beget."

I therefore strove to imagine this daughter. She would be robust, endowed with courage and judgment, capable of accompanying me in my future battles, and be devoted to my fame and my works. Because of her mother, she would be circumspect. I saw her upright, a shaft of a spear in her hand, a golden helmet on her head.

Thus Athena came from my brow and from Metis's body. My mind was so preoccupied that I was scarcely aware of pleasure. I was more conscious of surprise than gratification.

It is not true, as some have maintained, who no doubt confuse me with my father or, so as to injure my reputation, attributed his cruelty to me, that I devoured my cousin when she was pregnant; nor, indeed, is it true that I ordered my son Hephaestus to cleave my skull so that Athena might spring from it; and this for the very simple reason that the birth of Hephaestus, my twenty-fifth child, was not to take place for many millennia.

I *thought* Athena when begetting her; I really did imagine her; and this is what should be understood when it is said that she sprang fully armed from my head.

And since I have determined that my revelations to you shall be complete, you must know what happened afterwards.

That night, with the ardor of youth to expand its strength, I desired to honor my cousin once again; and, indeed, I was already at the business, and with greater pleasure than the first time, when Metis suddenly disengaged herself.

"You must beware," she said, "of inadvertently begetting a son who, from being born too soon, will be an anxiety to you and whose activities and impatience may compromise a reign you have yet to conquer. If you do not want to be dethroned, beget no son till your power is firmly established."

She saw my disappointment, and that I was in no mood to be content with mere words. She contrived to appease me by bending to my desire as a nymph leans over a spring.

Before falling asleep, I heard her say once again: "I am Prudence."

Our first mistresses leave a deep imprint on us. Later, it is we who mark the others.

The mixture of attraction and discretion with which extreme youth always inspires me is derived from Amaltheia; and if I am called prudent Zeus, despite so much apparent wantonness, it is to Metis I owe it.

In a god's due course, Athena was born, precisely as I had wished her to be.

My daughter Athena is tall and beautiful, though it must be admitted somewhat heavy in body. Her strong, proud features rather resemble mine. She has her mother's observant calm. She is above all goddess of Reason. So sure are her qualities of judgment and decision, so natural her aptitude for command, that I have often entrusted her with arbitrating the conflicts of mankind in my name. Often, too, since she is a brave warrior, I have lent her Aegis which renders its bearer invincible. Athena is a stranger to the allurements of the senses, which is not surprising when one considers the circumstances of her conception. She admires me so much that she has never desired to take a husband, for none who has presented himself has sufficiently resembled me. She has remained a virgin.

The Condition of Man
Before the War of the Gods.
The Opposing Forces.
The Search for Allies.

The struggle I undertook against my father Cronus occupied, both in preparation and fighting, ten years—ten great years of the world, you must understand, of which each, in making a complete circle of the months of the Great Clock, lasts rather more than twenty-four thousand of your years.

If you make the calculation, you will appreciate that the period which elapsed was that between the time when your only tools were knapped flints, and that other, under my reign, when you were endowed with fine bronze weapons, golden jewelry, woven cloth and laws for your cities.

For throughout the whole of Cronus's reign you were, so to speak, astray in the night.

You are surprised, I know, that your race could have passed from the Golden Age into this miserable darkness. The lack of any trace renders you incredulous of the existence of the happy times of Atlantis; and if it were not for the transmission of the Zodiac and the mysterious techniques evident in the building of your most ancient monuments, the very idea would be unacceptable to you.

Ask yourselves what would remain, two hundred and forty thousand years from now, of your methods, your powers and your works if some other gigantic catastrophe occurred at this moment. What trace would remain of your arts, of your buildings, of your machines and of your conquests, which would enable your remote descendants to know that you could light yourselves without smoke or flame, build towers one thousand feet high to live in, go down to the bottom of the sea, propel yourselves through the air in machines a thousand times heavier than you are, and that you held in your hands such tremendous energies that in liberating them you disintegrated both your works and yourselves? Where would your calculations be recorded? Where would your history be written? Would anyone ever believe that you had existed? And you are still only minor engineers. Have a care, I repeat, have a care!

Ten years of a god or ten years of a man, this is always the time youth needs to make itself known, acquire a position, and assert its rights. He who allows these ten years to go by without audacity, revolt or labor is preparing for himself a sad maturity, and his life, poor in works, much resembles non-existence.

When I consider, from my present position, the state of the world when I set out to liberate it, I conclude that ignorance is often a necessary condition for enterprise. It is not old men who make revolutions; and if there are sometimes old men at their head, it is because they had dreamed of revolution when they were twenty.

The undertaking, at first sight, might well have seemed mad. What allies had I? My two brothers, young gods who were as much novices as I, a nymph forsaken on an island, and my cousin Prudence, who was mainly concerned to conceal the support she was giving me—these were my troops.

Opposed to me were Cronus and his brothers the Titans, who had at their disposal all the forces and divinities of the universe. Life and death, fire and frost, the wind, the great effort the Earth makes to produce fruits and rich harvests, all these belonged to them, all these were subject to them. The giants, born of Uranus's wound and already in the pay of their elders, were everywhere creating a reign of terror and imposing a tyranny of which they were the only beneficiaries. Let us not mention man; he was so timid and oppressed, and labored so hard merely to exist, that he felt himself the slave of all nature.

But a prince is truly a prince only by the consent of those he governs. That Cronus should have needed the giants and furies, whom he paid, to impose his rule, was proof enough that it was not accepted with general satisfaction.

As soon as it became known that I existed, a secret but stubborn hope began to run through the whole of creation. And this glimmer of freedom having appeared, the yoke seemed to weigh more heavily on those who bore it.

The first encouragement I received was from my

uncle Oceanus who informed me that, if a struggle broke out between my father and myself, he would abstain from taking part in it. It was one way of supporting me; and the better to prove his good intentions towards me, he agreed that his wife Tethys should harbor my sister Hera, while one of their daughters, Cephira, offered my brother Poseidon asylum in the island of Rhodes.

Thus, of the four elements, one was already on my side; everything that derived from the liquid principle, seas, rivers, lakes and streams, and the divinities who ruled the waters and the species that inhabited them, were ready to side with me; the brooks babbled of my coming.

But I needed much more help; and it was supplied mostly by the goddesses.

I have already told how cruelly Cronus treated my mother Rhea. The other Titans, with the exception of Oceanus, behaved similarly towards their wives; and the mercenary giants had set about imitating them. In this regime of violence, the male principle wanted to be absolute, and everything that formed part of the female character—wisdom, grace, sweetness, tenderness and reverie—was despised and flouted.

The goddesses lived in complete subordination, and their only distraction from boredom was fear. They welcomed my youthful passion for liberty. I have loved them much, and this they have reciprocated. Nor have they failed to forgive me even for being faithful to none of them. I had to expend myself for all of them; and they made common cause.

At this time, my impulses drove me for preference towards those goddesses who could best help me in my struggle and ensure me effective allies. Do not blame me for this, nor deduce from it that I pretended to love merely to serve my ambitions and my war. It would be to take a very narrow view, and a false one. I have always sincerely loved those who, while loving me in return, furnished me with knowledge, weapons or support.

You have reached a point where you accord the title of "great love" only to devouring passions which destroy those who suffer them by leading them to inaction, confusion, abnegation, and various forms of madness. You apply to love all the terms applicable to fire: smoldering, glowing, blazing passion; and you talk of ashes.

But love is not only a flame; it is a forge. To love is to burn, of course; it is to consume each other, but in order to create together.

Themis.
The Site of Delphi.
The Two Stones.

When I was about to leave Prudence, she said: "I advise you to go in the first instance to our aunt Themis."

I therefore went to the shore you call Attica, crossed the isthmus, and followed the edge of the Gulf of Corinth. The Titans must have been looking for me elsewhere in the world, for the waters of the gulf were translucent and calm, and everything bore an appearance of happiness. From there, rising over the mountains, I reached a long, mysterious and tragic gorge, a valley shaped like a mouth, but curved as if to utter a groan. This is the site of Delphi.

Themis was standing naked and immobile between the two Phoedriades rocks, the Red and the Flaming, whose precipitous sides reflected the sun's rays onto her, like two gigantic mirrors. She seemed to me huge and to be covered in gold.

Her hair was parted in the center of her brow and framed her face in two equal bands. Her eyebrows were perfectly symmetrical, as were her nostrils; a perfect horizontal line could have been drawn between the nipples of her breasts. On her open palms reposed two stones of exactly similar weight and she held them at precisely the same level.

"You see," she said sadly, "I have nothing else to do."

Some eagles then came down from their eyrie, a ledge on the red cliff, and flew round my head, forming a moving, sumptuous crown.

"They, too, have recognized you," Themis said. "You are my nephew Zeus. I am the Law."

Then she added, pointing to the landscape before her: "Here my mother Gæa issued her oracles. And here I am supposed to issue mine. But who asks for them or listens to them these days?"

"I want," I replied, "to hear and to learn."

I learned from Themis the general laws of the universe, from which all other laws proceed. I learned that the function of justice, of which she is the guardian, is to preserve an equilibrium between the hostile forces which animate every action and every creation. I learned that order founded on compulsion is a false order.

"To rule in order to rule is not an end in itself," Themis added. "Think of your father's errors, and the disasters into which he has plunged the world. To impose oneself without having proposals to make is merely fatal pride; and even to liberate is useless if one has not considered proper measures for administering the liberated. Be careful to prepare what you offer the world."

We prepared.

77

While making love, my aunt Themis insisted on remaining standing. Indeed, she went so far as to refuse to put down the two round stones she carried on her palms, and took care to maintain their equilibrium throughout our embrace.

When I pressed her to lie down, she resisted me with her firm breasts and beautiful smooth shoulders, and she said: "The Law receives the scepter; but never lies down."

Themis showed no reluctance, nor was she in the least alarmed. She offered herself simply, but remained completely immobile; she was not cold, but concentrated; and far from feeling little, I suspect, on the contrary, that she felt a double gratification from watching so impassively the flowering of her own pleasure. She thus proved to me that love is also a mental act, and that lucidity is no hindrance to ecstasy.

An older god than I might have been wearied by having to furnish this vertical effort alone. But this was only my second affair; and this tall, straight goddess, with her solid golden thighs, passive in appearance but only the better to possess both herself and her lover, and wholly consenting provided only one allowed her to remain perfectly still, exacerbated my desire.

Three times a day, at the rising of the sun, at its zenith and at its setting, and for three consecutive days, the eagles flew regally about our brows, encompassing our giant unions.

However, I constantly bore Metis's advice in mind: "Daughters, nothing but daughters, so long as you are not king."

78

The Seasons & the Fates.

A̲nd thus, the first day, at the three hours of light, Themis and I conceived the three Seasons. They are called Eunomia, Dice and Irene; that is to say, Good Laws, Justice and Peace. The Athenians also call them Seed, Growth and Fruit. Nor are they wrong.

The first to be born of Law and Power, the Seasons have the duty of presiding over the regular cycles of the vegetable world, and also over the ordering of human societies. These two functions are not incompatible.

Nature is for man a school of wisdom, and he who watches over the harvest knows the value of peace.

My daughters, the Seasons, go by field and street, holding a flower in their hands. Mortals, why do you not imitate them?

Wild or cultivated, a flower is a mysterious manifestation of passing beauty. It invites you to marvel, and therefore to gratitude; it invites you to thought, and therefore to tolerance. A fragile culmination, it is a moment of happiness, and demands restraint in action. I often see you, mortals my children, proudly clasping a weapon or a purse; but I see you all too rarely carrying a flower in your hands.

On the second day, Themis and I conceived three more daughters: Clotho, Lachesis and Atropos. You know them well, and call them the Fates; they have a somber reputation among you because of the last, whose duty it is to cut the thread of your years. You curse her.

But do you ever think of thanking Clotho for having drawn from the huge, grey fleece of the uncreated the first fiber of your particular destiny? Would you not like to kiss her hand?

Do you not think it a miracle that in the great lottery of life, among the millions of billions of numbers, yours should have been drawn? To be born, my sons, is to be one of the elect!

And do you never spare a thought for Lachesis, the most active and the busiest of all the divinities, dear overworked Lachesis who knows neither rest nor sleep? She rolls the thread round her distaff—and this is easily said! You do not realize that she has ceaselessly to watch the thread, strengthen it when it grows too thin, twist the fibers while you do all you can to part them, and with a quick knot preserve your life each time it is in danger of breaking. Who alters the direction of your vehicle before you hit the fatal tree, sends the unexpected rescuer when you are on the point of drowning, and deflects the projectile from your artery? It is Lachesis, invariably Lachesis.

And if you do happen to think of her, you are quite capable of imagining her with one thread on her hands —your own particular thread. Yet, at this very moment, she has more than two thousand million threads to control; and Clotho is continually giving her yet more work to do.

Two thousand million threads, two thousand million spindles! Think of the immense amount of work Lachesis has; and understand why it is I recommend you not to procreate without reflection, why I advise you to be careful in your enterprises, of your food, of every step you take, and why I exhort you not to threaten each other with your armaments.

For so great a labor, I should perhaps have begotten more Fates. But at the beginning of my reign, they seemed sufficient for their task; I did not know that so many of you would want to live. Alas, one cannot think of everything; and Themis herself, preoccupied only with the threefold ordinance, had not foreseen it.

Mortals my sons, do not blame the Fates. They are not the Destinies; they are only the guardians. They stand, indefatigable customs' officers, at the frontier of your awareness and my power.

The Hesperides.

However, on the third morning, foreseeing the questions which you, in your obstinacy, would not fail to ask, I inquired of Themis: "What do you know of the nature of the Destinies? Are they random or deliberate?"

For a long moment she remained silent, her golden eyes fixed on the dawn breaking over the hills; then, assuming her oracular voice, she replied: "The Destinies are fatality in continuous creation."

I will give you a moment in which to reflect. . . . Have you done so? Very well. Then those among you, my sons, who have understood may ask your way of the Hesperides.

For that day, Themis and I conceived the three Hesperides: Aegle, Erytheia and Arethusa of Evening, three nymphs who are also customs' officers, but of the future.

I assigned to them for their abode the remains of the gardens of Uranus. They look after the trees with golden apples which my grandfather had planted to feed his beloved Atlantes.

The mountain, often covered with snow, which stands above the principal orange-grove of the Hesperides, is called Atlas. You need to have seen Marrakesh beneath the silver moonlight of winter nights to know what a garden may be. But there are others, almost equally enchanted, scattered over western Africa and even in the islands of the ocean.

Aegle cultivates the tangerine, bright as the sun in the morning sky; Erytheia watches over the lemon, golden as the sun at noon; and Arethusa plucks the orange of the setting sun.

Open these fruits that are as round as worlds. Their flesh divides delicately like the hours of the day or the months of the Earth; their clear juice contains principles of strength.

The Hesperides are best known to you for the great service they did my son Heracles and which contributed so much to the spread of the cultivation of citrous fruits in diverse countries. But their role is not limited to these horticultural labors.

Their duty is to guide the traveler, be he man or god, on the road to the future; they are the nymphs of that form of discovery which consists of a wider knowledge of the universe and the laws which govern it. They often travel themselves and visit places where great thoughts are about to come to birth. They were seen on the banks of the Nile when Pythagoras, Herodotus and Plato, those glories of your race, each in turn visited the temples of upper Egypt. They were seen swimming off the Sicilian beaches when Archimedes, that other descendant of my son Hermes, was in contemplation there. And from the report I have had drawn up of your history during the time I was asleep, I suspect that the Hesperides were haunting the neighborhood of Palos, Cadiz and the Tagus in the century of Columbus, that great-nephew of my brother Poseidon.

Each evening, carrying a golden fruit, the Hesperides meet at some point on the western shore and, going forward to the edge of sunken Atlantis, watch the sun drop slowly into it. They receive their orders for the morrow.

This is the best hour at which to invoke them.

To hope is to conceive on the threshold of each

night the next day's work. And only they make progress in the adventure of living who are prepared each morning to transform into action their plans of the night before.

Were Themis and I a little weary that third day? I must admit that the Hesperides have neither the vigor nor the precision of movement which everyone agrees their elder sisters, the Seasons and the Fates, possess. Even their features are not so firmly drawn. They manifest a certain indolence in their activities, and you have often to question them several times before you can extract an answer. Do not expect them to trace your path for you with precision, and still less that they will smooth it before you. They will indicate a direction. But you will not be saved from losing yourself among the sands.

Departure from Delphi.
The Oracle of Gæa.

I left Delphi at the hour the eagles go to sleep. Themis asked me to come back when I should have to issue oracles of my own. I promised, and in all good faith.

I could imagine myself spending my life as a god

with Themis willingly enough. Her beautiful immo-
bility, her calm assurance, induced a feeling of protec-
tiveness, equilibrium and peace. What better could
one hope for?

It is thus, particularly when we are young, that we
make promises of this kind and of which the only en-
during quality is regret at having made them or re-
morse at having betrayed them. They are the sign of
a passing lassitude which makes the imagination falter.
We consent to see the other as he sees himself, that is
to say unique in the universe. He becomes the center,
the essence, the refuge. And we dream of taking our
rest in the very arms that have provoked our fatigue.

This is true not only of humans and gods, but also
of the causes we embrace. The efforts we have devoted
to them, the strength we have lavished on them, limit
our outlook and prevent our seeing anything else but
them. . . .

As I was passing through the winding gorges that
lead down into the valley, I heard a grave, sulky voice
say: "I see you talk to everyone except me."

I started, and stared vainly round at the shadows.
For a moment I feared it was my father lying in ambush behind some mountain. But it was a female voice,
and it went on: "And yet I am older than those chits
of girls, who have been teaching you so well. I, too,
issue oracles, and have been doing so for far longer
than they."

"Who are you? Where are you?" I asked.

"People who don't recognize me are most ungrateful!" the voice went on. "Without me, and the advice

I gave your mother to conceal your birth, you would not be big and strong as you are, nor wantoning, whether lying or standing, with the girls of my family."

Then I understood, and cried: "Grandmother? Is it you, grandmother? But where are you?"

"Beneath your feet."

I threw myself to the ground.

"All thanks to you, dear grandmother Gæa!" I said. "I cannot tell you how grateful I am to you."

"Oh, it wasn't for you I did it! It was against the others."

"Forgive my surprise," I went on. "The reason I did not recognize you sooner was because Themis told me you no longer issued oracles."

"My daughter the Law always thinks she knows everything."

And I heard a long laugh in the depths.

"Besides, the whole family want me to keep silence," Gæa added.

"Not I, grandmother, not I!"

There was a long pause. My ear was glued to the stones. Was the low murmur I heard the Earth's breathing, or her secret meditation? At last the voice came up to me again.

"You will succeed in conquering your father," she said, "only if you free the One-Eyed and the Hundred-Handed."

At that time, I still knew nothing of the Hundred-Handed, not even their name, nor did I know what sort of mother Gæa was, jealous of her children, supporting one son against another according to her mood, and always ready to hate the last whose victory she had assisted.

I asked: "Grandmother, who are the One-Eyed and the Hundred-Handed, and where shall I find them?"

"That's up to you, my boy; I've told you enough."

I insisted; I waited; but I could get nothing more from her. No doubt, Gæa had already turned against me. I got to my feet, perplexed, and continued on my way.

I never had any further direct communication with my grandmother the Earth. Whatever the difficulties she created for me later by her unstable character, I cannot deny the great service she did me on this occasion.

The Spring of Forgetfulness.
The Blue Valley.
Meeting with Memory.

I was walking through the night, seeking a sheltered spot in which to think and sleep. I was going towards the East, hoping that the sun at his rising would enlighten me as to the meaning of the Earth's obscure oracle. And, indeed, it was on my road that I saw the light; but it was not the sun's. Here is another precept. The things we really desire and for which we are prepared to make an effort generally happen, but never in the way we had imagined.

Having covered about two hundred of your stadia, I entered another gorge, much narrower than that of Delphi. There water rustled, murmured, trembled and whispered on all sides. All the voices of the waters seemed to be united there. The air was sublimely warm and clear. Above the rocks, the Milky Way appeared so dense with stars that one could have drawn its outline, a tall goddess softly draped in twinkling sleep.

"What a wonderful place the Earth is," I thought. "Thank you, grandmother!"

And yet in this perfect place I felt a certain melancholy, as it were a sad sense of loneliness. For, indeed, happiness may be qualified by a vague sorrow, for lack of someone to share it with. I thought of Themis. Why had I not asked her to accompany me, rather than wait for me between her two cliffs?

I lay down. Certain fears of childhood returned to assail me. I felt less sure of my future victory.

The scent of the grass on which I was lying made me think of Amaltheia.

Dear little Amaltheia! Suppose I went one day to take her from the island and keep her always beside me?

I put out my hand to make sure that Aegis was within my reach. Prudence. . . .

Indeed, I felt rather weary that night.

I put my head into the nearest spring. I let the water

trickle over my face; it was like a divinely light, cool hand placed on my brow. I drank in long gulps. No water had ever seemed so delectable to me before. I immediately fell asleep.

I do not know how long my sleep lasted. What is a god's night—seven hundred thousand of yours? Or only the time it takes for a man's life to be resolved? I do not know. When I woke up, the sun had already made a great part of his journey. All was blue about me. The limpid dome of the sky was blue; the little stream cascading down between the blue-grey rocks was blue; the springs were blue under the blue shade of the trees; the foliage was blue-green, as were the weeds and water-cress; the stones beneath the glistening water were silver-blue; the misty light outlining the distant shapes of the hills was blue; and blue, bluer than all the rest, were the eyes gazing down at me.

I sat up.

"Where am I?" I cried. "And who am I?"

I was in the grip of agonizing anxiety. I could remember neither how I had come there, nor when. I could remember nothing I had ever done, no single face, nor any place. I knew nothing at all, not even my own name. I merely had the feeling that I had lived, as one remembers vaguely after a dream that one has dreamed.

The blue eyes watching me narrowed in an expression of amusement and tenderness; and the goddess, whose eyes they were, said: "You have drunk of the spring of forgetfulness. Its waters come from Lethe, at which the souls of the dead drink to lose the memory of their terrestrial lives, and also, on returning, the souls who are to assume new bodies so that they may forget their stay in the Infernal Regions. Thus each may believe he was a new soul, when in fact it is merely drawn from the common stock of his species and of the universe. And it is right that each individual should believe he has a soul peculiar to himself, since he is, for a moment, unique."

I listened, but without real understanding. I was concentrating on trying to remember my name.

"Both to the living and to immortals this spring brings forgetfulness of the past. During your sleep, you were absent from yourself. The errors, fears and regrets, which form in the mind an obstacle to knowledge and action, have been dissolved. Now turn to this other spring, which is mine, and drink again."

I obeyed. At once, I felt myself possessed of a great clarity, an absolute light that did not emanate from the sun but from myself. I felt as if I had at my disposal a vast apparatus of crystal designed to reflect the world in its totality, both in its extent and in its movement, and whose thousand transparent cogs were merely waiting to begin to turn.

"I am Memory, your father's sister," the goddess said.

She talked for nine days.

Mnemosyne, Memory, was the eldest daughter of my grandfather Uranus, and was tall and beautiful as her sister Themis, but of greater freedom and carelessness of gesture. In the hollow of her elbow, her transparent skin revealed a tracery of veins similar to the network of streams and rivers. And when she shook her fair hair, she seemed to be shaking stardust. Her voice was a song, her words music.

She talked for nine days. I have never known another goddess, nor any mortal woman, who was capable of talking so long without ever mentioning herself. By this she taught me that the self-importance we assume cuts us off from knowledge, and that we would be better mirrors of the universe if we were less concerned about our own image.

And yet Memory had secret griefs. Were they due to the tragedies she had witnessed, to nostalgia for her beautiful lost Atlantis, or to her long loneliness between the two springs?

Everything I have told you about the origins of our family at the beginning of this story, I have learned from Memory.

She talked for nine days; and for nine days I listened to her, entranced. Must I remind you again that each of those days was equivalent to one of your millennia?

We made love for nine nights. My fair aunt seemed to be clasping her regret for her dead father in her arms.

We had nine daughters.

The Muses: Their Nature,
Their Functions.

Though you often forget their names, Memory's daughters are of all the divinities those whom you, mortals, believe you know best, or rather those who you believe know you best. I see few among you who, because they have taken a few zither or dancing lessons, have once donned the cothurnus on a school stage, or have rhymed a few stanzas one evening of adolescence, have not believed themselves singled out by a Muse. And the same is true of those who, to listen to them, have lacked only the time to write the poignant drama of their lives, or that farce they perceive other people's lives to be.

You are not wholly wrong. The Muses have looked at you all, one after the other; but not with lovers' eyes. They have looked at you as good housewives select a chicken in the market—"Not that one; not that one"—or again like an overseer in past times buying new slaves for an estate—"Let's look at your eyes, your hands. If you work well, you'll be freed." They have observed you and looked you up and down as carefully as a recruiting sergeant; and those they think suited to frenzy and loneliness, they seduce with

the promise: "You shall be praised as the gods are."
But the misfortune of those they select is that they are
not gods, but only men with the dreams of gods. And
both their works and their sufferings are derived from
the disparity between their two natures.

You will understand the kind of conversation I had
with Memory that first day when I tell you that the
first of our nine daughters to be begotten was Calliope
of the beautiful voice, the Muse of the heroic epic.
Calliope presides over legend, the collective tradi-
tions of the most distant memories of your race and
mine. She is the keeper of myths, which are the sym-
bolic epitomes of the generalities that concern you
as well as the ancestors of all philosophic thought. She
inspires the poems and the archetypal stories which
help you to situate yourselves in the universe. Calliope
is the mother of Orpheus, whom she had by her half-
brother, my son Apollo.

The next night Clio, the Muse of history, was begotten. She was to serve as her mother's assistant and
keep an account of everything that happened on Earth
during my reign. But Clio did not always give me complete satisfaction. Indolent in youth, she was content
to follow her eldest sister and unburden onto her the
task she should have performed. There were many
great deeds at the time of the origins of nations which
are considered fables because they have been recorded
for you by Calliope instead of Clio. I suspect her of
having fallen in love with my son Ares, or Mars as
you prefer to call him, because for a long while she
seemed to care for nothing but the clash of battle.

93

She has recorded the names of the commanders of the squadrons which besieged Thebes, but she has failed to note who invented the windlass and the pulley, the ladder, the set-square, the brick and its cement, the keystone, and papyrus. They were divine envoys, of course, but they nevertheless had men's hands!

Clio began to show a little activity only when my son Hermes brought her writing. But, imbued with the prejudices of her birth, she was more interested in princes than in ordinary people. A weaver had no merit in her eyes unless he had assassinated a king, nor a shepherd unless he had been a queen's lover. Jealous of the honor accorded Calliope, she wished to shine and please by seeking to flatter the powerful and attract the crowd. Nevertheless, as she grew older, she realized her errors and, repenting of her frivolity, tried to make amends. She went through all her files, was concerned to find so many lacunae and endeavored to fill them by imagination rather than fact. But nowadays there is no stopping her. She notes everything, from the immense to the infinitely small, checks, compares, deduces, covers every field, including that of Themis, and would like to make herself out to be more important than I am.

Poor Clio! We must not criticize her too harshly. She has rarely had the lovers she desired and her temper has suffered from it. Ares preferred to her Polyhymnia, her sister begotten on the third night.

When we begot Polyhymnia, the Muse of sacred songs, Memory had just taught me the power of sounds when they are modulated in accordance with certain rhythms. There are some that instill courage, destroying the fear of pain and even the terror of death; some that sustain effort; some that cure the ills of the soul by appeasing the sufferings of the body; some that put the consciousness to sleep, but also others that increase awareness and dispose the mind to the ecstasies of contemplation. Polyhymnia presides over the incantations which move the gods.

The fourth day was that on which Memory became so nostalgic over her recollections of Atlantis. Her eyes constantly became veiled with tears on behalf of all the living things that flew, ran, grew or flowered around us.

"I remember the day Uranus blew air into certain kinds of seaweed so that they might float," she said. "Look at that beetle crawling in the dust; it was his first design for a man's skull."

When night fell, she said: "Listen to the stars. The Atlantes could hear them revolve."

That night Euterpe, the flute-player, was begotten. She is the Muse of wind blown into pipes, the Muse of the air that vibrates under the plucked string. She has at her disposal numerical variations which are reminiscent of those of the creation of species and provide terrestrial ears with some approximation to the music of the spheres. She is Music.

The fifth day, which marked the middle of our nuptials, was also their climax. Mnemosyne seemed perfectly happy; she was in love and felt that she was loved. We knew each other well enough for mutual understanding, but we still had more to learn about each other. A pose, a gesture, a movement of the fingers, a glance were enough to make me understand what Memory wished to tell me. We were aware of all the natural harmonies and they sustained our happiness. We revolved about ourselves and each other. She was the earth and the sun. I was delighted that Memory should have remained so young, vital and wanton. I threw her over my knee, her hair almost touching the ground; she was the waterfall, and I the rock. I raised her at arms' length towards the light; I was the tree, and she the sap and the leaves. Her hand, when open like a calyx, represented the flower, and when closed was the image of the fruit. Our daughter Terpsichore is the Muse of the dance. Her name means plenitude.

After so much leaping and bounding, the next day was more or less one of idleness and languor. We loved each other as much as ever, but with less impetuosity. Two or three times, I noticed that Memory was beginning to repeat herself. I realized that, if I remained too long, I should become bored. As we were walking hand in hand in the blue valley, I said to her: "When I am king, I shall found a town near this place in memory of our love. It will be called Livadia, the town of springs, and your pilgrims will be able to halt there."

I had expressed this thought out of amiability and to show my gratitude. But Memory realized I would soon be leaving her, and her sadness returned. We were each thinking of ourselves.

That night, on her warm shoulder, I was more in

search of tenderness than love; but Memory taught me the power words have to awaken desire, sustain pleasure and prolong it. And so Erato, who presides over lyric and elegy, was begotten. She tells of the happiness and unhappiness of living, of the sweetness and pain of loving; and she expresses man's emotion in face of the universe and his regret that his stay is transient. Erato is also the Muse of the erotic imagination. She has always refused to wear any clothing at all; she finds comfort in nakedness.

On the seventh day, I asked Memory how to reach the Hundred-Handed and free them. For I had recovered all my personal memories, and could now put them in their right place among the memories of the world. I no longer had to think: "Why has such and such a thing happened? What is the significance of this meeting, or that event?" Thanks to Memory, I understood the continuities and relationships. I had learned to recognize and therefore to deduce, reflect and think.

At my question, Memory showed signs of fear and anxiety.

"Must you really free them?" she asked.

I told her of Gæa's oracle.

"I know, I know everything," my aunt said. "But will I have to record tragedies, disasters, ravages and catastrophes all over again?"

"Have you not taught me that nothing can be created without the confrontation of two forces? The world is unhappy living under my father's rule. . . ."

"And things have reached a point at which only

violence can save the world from its misfortunes. I know all that. I shall therefore tell you that the Cyclopes and the Hecatoncheires are shut up in Tartarus. Tartarus is the bottom of the world, the void created by the absence of manifest things, the non-sky, and the anti-life. You will be afraid when you go there. The door behind which the Hundred-Handed are imprisoned is fastened by eighty-six padlocks. The key is to be found in the infinitely small."

I thought for a moment and murmured: "I understand."

"Then you must reveal to no one what you have understood," Memory said.

She was lost in thought for a moment, then added: "I hope your rebellion will spare my blue valley. For if what is here perished, I do not think either you or any god could renew it."

Melpomene, the Muse of tragedy, in which is represented the struggle of adverse Fates, was the work of that night.

Was it to give me confidence before the ordeals that awaited me that, on the eighth morning, Memory contrived to turn everything to laughter? When faced with the elements of tragedy, we have only to alter the associations of our ideas a little for it to become burlesque.

Both laughter and fear are born of the unusual, of a break in the rhythm, of an error in the ordering of the numbers of nature or thought. And fear assails you when you feel you are threatened by this error. If you are shown a man with a lion's head, you tremble because you are afraid of the lion. But if you are shown a man afflicted with a donkey's tail, you will shake with laughter, because you feel stronger than a donkey's rear, and the unusual is here to your advantage.

The same is true at sight of the errors of your own kind, and of the difficulties and weaknesses that cause their troubles. Laughter is always a way of asserting your superiority. That is why you so much enjoy comedy in the theater. But the supreme superiority consists in being able to laugh at oneself. The lucid and mocking Thalia was begotten the eighth night.

On the ninth morning, Memory woke up with a graver air than she had ever shown before.

All that day, she talked to me of nothing but man.

"Watch over him; he is my father's masterpiece— an unfinished masterpiece. He had no time to perfect him. He wanted man to be his friend; and a friend is always an equal. Uranus has taken his dream with him into the sky; but the combinations of the Number of man are far from being exhausted. Try to see that man fulfills his dream."

I promised Memory to do my best. Our last daughter was called Urania, in memory of the founder. She is the Muse of mathematics, astronomy, physics and biology, the persistent and precise researcher, whose gaze pierces the invisible, measures the galaxy and the atom, and calculates the paths of the infinite. She is the supreme alchemist, ceaselessly correlating the results of her discoveries; and she is also poetry, since, revealing as she does hitherto unperceived relationships, she expresses herself in symbols and is constantly inventing her own language. She traces the circles of progress with her compass.

That last night, after we had begotten Urania, we could not sleep. Then Memory, for the first and only time, talked modestly of herself.

"To live merely for this memory is a melancholy happiness," she said. "Memory is useful only to create. We have created. Now I shall remember. . . ."

She kissed my forehead, but less like a mistress than a mother.

"Suppose I offered to marry Memory? Suppose I promised to come back and remain faithful to her?" I thought in one of those false fits of kindness one knows will never be put into effect.

She must have guessed my thoughts, for she added: "I am too old for you. I have kept you as long as I could and given you all I could. Your destiny leads you towards others."

In that grey hour when thought slumbers, as Memory seemed to be asleep, I parted her fine blonde hair to gaze on her face for the last time. In the dawning day, I could see the fine star-shaped lines near her temple. A tear was drying there. I left silently.

Oh, Memory, supreme educator! I came to you an adolescent. I left you a man. I was aware of it; and I was moved.

My sons, when in search of the remains of vanished ages you travel from Athens to Delphi, halt in the blue valley of Livadia and drink from its two springs.

Mount Helicon stands nearby. I made a present of

it to the nine sisters; they look on it rather as a child-hood home and like to meet there. One studies in the shade of the pines, another recites to the horizon, and a third records. Terpsichore dances among the bushes to Euterpe's flute. They allow themselves to be contemplated. But none of them will choose you to share the agony and honor of creating, if you have not first been taught by their mother. What you call "doing the humanities" is above all "doing the divinities."

Have no fear of finding Memory grown old. The centuries of my reign are a trifle in proportion to the whole expanse of time; they have scarcely touched her.

Do not forget to tell Memory that I remember her.

Eurynome.
The Graces.

A nd now, forward to Tartarus!" I thought as I ran down the hills. I was hurrying on, breathing great gulps of air, both as an anodyne to the melancholy of parting and to the anxiety as to what awaited me. I soon came to a shore of many promontories and quiet coves in which the sea lay peculiarly calm.

This shore was later to be called the Gulf of the Alcyons.

I was on my way, my heels sinking into the sand, when I heard someone hailing me.

"Zeus! My cousin Zeus!"

The voice came from the sea. I saw a goddess, up to the waist in the water, signaling wildly to me with her arms.

I put a finger to my lips; the era had not yet come to cry my name so loudly. But the imprudent goddess went on calling me. I signed to her to join me.

"I cannot!" she shouted. "I cannot come out of the sea. I have to be helped. Zeus! My cousin Zeus!"

From a distance, she seemed very beautiful, and seemed also to be double. I mean that, in the bright light, her stomach and breasts were repeated upside down in the water, and the reflection was quivering as if with the tremblings of love.

I glanced at the sun to determine the hour. I had plenty of time to reach Tartarus before evening. My curiosity had a good excuse to justify it; her shouting had to be stopped, or the Titans would gather.

So I entered the sea and went to the goddess. Nor was I disappointed. No more exquisite bosom than hers could be imagined. Her hair, all wet and twisted, fell over her shoulder like a brass tress; the drops of water on her breasts were trickling pearls.

"I am Eurynome, or Wide-Sharing, the sister of Metis," she said.

Eurynome had enormous eyes, and their expression was at once frightened and imploring.

"Look," she said.

She lay back and floated. From the hips down her body was that of a fish.

Erect again, she explained: "I am the daughter of Oceanus. I was the wife of the giant Ophion, one of Cronus's wicked assistants. We lived on Olympus. Oh, what a splendid time that was! So spendid indeed, that Cronus wished to stay there permanently. Ophion was so proud to have his master living in his house that he did not know what to do with himself. Olympus became the scene of the grossest cruelty and brutality. Ophion, in his servile vanity, modeled himself entirely on Cronus. And Cronus does not like his brother Oceanus. This was enough to make Ophion get rid of me. I was deceived, maltreated and brutalized. Those two wild beasts laughed at having reduced me to the condition of the lowliest servant. In the end, they chased me away with kicks and stones. I took refuge with my parents and, in my distress, besought them to change me in such a way that it would be impossible for me ever to leave the sea. Do you think I can still be loved in my present state?"

Eurynome clung to my neck with her wet arms; I could feel her fins clasping my legs. Her lips had a strange savor, fresh and salty. Oh, wisdom, promises, faithfulness! Turning my head, I seemed to discern Memory's blue eyes on the crest of the hills. I had left her scarcely three hours ago. But she would have to get used to it, since she was destined to see everything that happened. . . .

The sea is an arrant bawd. She supports your body, slyly caresses your most sensitive parts, and her waves impose their rhythm on desire. Warm of torso and cold of legs, I yielded easily enough. After all, I was setting off to war. . . .

"What kind of a giant is Ophion?" I asked Eurynome a little later.

"A frightful brute," she said. "I hate myself for having had to submit to him. I never knew with him what I have just experienced in your arms; never, I swear it."

Did she think I was so much in love with her that she must already appease my jealousy? What did I care that she had belonged to another? I was gathering information about one of the enemies I was going to fight.

"Did you have any children by him?" I asked her.

"Three. But so as to be as like Cronus as possible he devoured them."

"How fortunate," I said.

It was a just but ill-timed remark, for Eurynome cried: "I would like to have others."

"Well, a daughter has no doubt already been begotten," I said to quiet her.

"Another. I want another. It would make me so happy!"

And her soft fins clasped my hips. I watched the sun moving up the sky.

With her head hidden in the hollow of my shoulder, Eurynome murmured: "Later on, we shall go to live on Olympus. You will turn Ophion out and take me back there. From its height we shall contemplate happiness. Promise me that we shall live on Olympus!"

"Of course, of course," I said.

"We shall stroll among the cypresses."

"Are there cypresses on Olympus?"

"No, but there are down below. We shall go down to them in the evening. You will carry me in your arms. Cypresses are so beautiful."

"Very beautiful indeed; it's the most beautiful of trees."

Poor Eurynome! Her misfortunes had driven her crazy. What would she have done on the summits, beating the clouds with her salmon's tail? But perhaps she was not deceived, and was merely indulging in the sad pleasure of illusions that know they are illusions.

But she had moved me, and the sea was lulling me, and I responded to her desire a second time.

I thought, after that, I could escape. But she at once began shouting: "Zeus, my cousin Zeus, my dear love, don't leave me! Don't abandon me!"

I felt a momentary sympathy with the appalling Ophion.

Eurynome was thrashing about amid a great splashing of water and shedding tears more salt than the sea. I was still afraid that the Titans would hear her shouting my name. To what surrenders we are compelled by fear of other people!

For the third time I set about quieting her frenzy. My ardor had cooled considerably; and it was rather a desire to murder her that she saw in my eyes; and this put an end to Eurynome's ardor.

"You don't understand," she said querulously. "I am Wide-Sharing. I want only to give all, and give it all to you."

"The greatest gifts you could give me," I replied, "would be your silence and my freedom."

"You'll regret me. You'll never meet another goddess capable of loving you so well."

"You reassure me, Eurynome. A little less would be quite enough."

"I really have no luck," she said.

And she sank into the pillow of the sea to stifle her sobs.

I must confess that Eurynome was one mistress too many. I would have lost little by doing without her. Nor did she even teach me to beware of sirens of her kind. For this is the least vigilant form of caution; it is lulled by every change of appearance, and I have committed the same error with many others merely because they had no scales below their hips.

I was concerned about the children to whom Eurynome would give birth. Luckily, the three girls take after their father as far as their legs are concerned. When it came to giving them names, I rather lacked imagination. I called them Aglaia, Euphrosyne and Thaleia, which somewhat resembled names already in use.

They are never apart, and always hold each other

by the shoulder, one of them invariably turned to look in the opposite direction to the others, which is pretty clear evidence of their lack of enthusiasm for enterprise and activity. They are the three Graces; and their beauty is equaled only by their indolence.

I have tried to give them various tasks to perform. They sometimes help the Seasons and the Hesperides with their horticultural work. Under the direction of the Muses, they wove—but with incredible slowness —Harmony's robe. If one gets very angry, they can be persuaded to do a certain amount of housework. They are quite good at doing the flowers.

Considering what little part they take in the world's work, they have an impressive number of worshipers. All the self-styled great artists, who do nothing but contemplate dreams of what they could do, the women, whose most constant occupation is to admire their own bodies in looking-glasses, and the idle, who consider the ability to appreciate and criticize other people's work an important function, devote a particular veneration to the Graces.

Poor cousin Eurynome! I shall complete her story by telling you that she later tried to join me. She left the sea, swam up rivers and streams, hoisted herself onto the bank and, dragging her fins through the dust, undertook an impossible climb. Moreover, the unhappy, crazy woman had mistaken the mountain. She climbed Mount Lycæus believing it was Olympus. With her elbows all bloody, leaving scales on the bushes, she reached Phigalie, and got no farther. Her temple stands there in a wood of cypresses.

However, no meeting is ever completely useless. It was Eurynome who first gave me the idea of establishing myself on Olympus. I live there, but not with her.

THE FOURTH EPOCH

Ordeal and Power

The Padlocks of Tartarus.
Crossing the Infernal Regions.
Freeing the One-Eyed &
the Hundred-Handed.

I shall not describe to you the road I took to go down to Tartarus; your eyes would be powerless to picture it. One must have divine perception to get there and one cannot express what one sees there in words.

And yet, observing you as I talk to you, it seems to me that you have recently manufactured certain apparatuses that make up for your blindness, and that you have also discovered a system of numeration for calculating your inventory of the invisible. Have you already got there? Have some among you followed the precepts of Urania so well that they have led you to the point I imagine?

I rejoice at it and yet it arouses my anxiety. I hope you have not trespassed in error on some part of the territory controlled by Thanatos of the black wings. The boundaries of life and non-life, of the world and the anti-world, are not as precisely drawn as the banks of your rivers. . . .

I had to cross the Infernal Regions. It is the first part of the journey, the passage from life to death, which is the zone of terror. Though I knew I was immortal, I will not conceal from you the fact that I was appallingly afraid. The long glissade seems endless; there are hands one cannot seize or which dissolve as you clasp them; there are hand-holds that crumble as you try to clutch them; the light fails, the cold burns, the fire freezes. . . . I am sorry, my sons, that you must all cross this threshold and by such a passage. The thought of it often makes me indulgent towards your faults.

After that things become quieter. Of its own accord the mind turns to oblivion and silence. Once the consciousness is obliterated, you cannot tell either the duration or extent of your stay in that abyss where all life ceases and withers to return to the great initial mass, while waiting for the Destinies to recompose it in a different way.

Tartarus is still farther down, not, as is carelessly said, in the depths of the Earth, but in the depths of the principle of the Earth. Even the notions of above and below no longer have their usual meaning there.

Nor shall I tell you how I acquired the key to the padlocks of Tartarus. I fear you may have found it on your own; and these rumors in space, which awakened me, make me fear the use to which you may put it. There are, indeed, periods of acceleration of knowledge foretold in your destiny. But beware of this very acceleration. Incomplete powers are the most dangerous. Follow my example, I entreat you, and, before encroaching on the invisible, remember the advice of Memory and follow the counsels of Prudence.

I came to the door which barred the dungeon of the One-Eyed and the Hundred-Handed. It was of lattice-work. I expected, in my anxiety, to see fearsome, roaring monsters, their strength and furious limbs mingled in continuous battle. Imagine my surprise! The blockheads were asleep. There was merely a minute sound of snoring, imperceptible to any but a divine ear, which revealed the presence of some slumbering energy in those logs. A Cyclops with his eye shut is no more than a piece of wood or stone. A Hecatoncheire with his arms folded looks like an old root, or a fragment of ore in its matrix of Earth. And indeed, seen in the depths of Tartarus, they seemed no more than tiny little roots, infinitesimal pebbles, sand, sawdust, nothing. Had I known less than I did, I would have paid no attention to them and treated them as so much negligible dust.

I assumed my best voice, whetted my eloquence and spoke to the dust thus:

"Radiant descendants of ancestor Chaos, powerful sons of Earth and Sky, you have been ignominiously accused of misdeeds for which you were not responsible; you have been betrayed by your elder brothers whom you served devotedly. They ordered you to perform the most noxious duties and then imprisoned you in this dungeon. I have come to free you. But in exchange for the freedom I bring you, you will from now on obey me, and only me. Your mother herself, concerned for her fate and yours, commands this. Together, we shall attack the Titans and their leader, Cronus the impostor, Cronus the cruel, who mutilated your beloved father, robbed him of his power, and for too many long eras has held the world in thrall. You must act only on my orders, deploy your strength only at my command. I shall use you only to destroy evil and establish right. We shall have a hard task, but together we shall triumph. Peace and prosperity will be the reward of our victory."

This speech, of which I feel rather proud, might seem to some people lacking in originality. The fact is that Clio has since collected a great many which seem to come from the same mold. Be kind enough to recognize that my proclamation was the first of its kind and that in the circumstances it was not lacking in invention.

However, the Cyclopes and the Hecatoncheires never so much as moved. Not a hair stirred, not a muscle twitched. They were utter logs, logs of dust. I decided to think rather than take offense. I realized that these shriveled colossi had no faculty of personal decision. Setting them in motion was entirely dependent on the will of whoever commanded them.

I called them by name: "Arges! Brontes! Steropes!"

Three phosphorescent eyes opened in the depths of the cavern.

I called: "Cottos! Briareus! Gyges!"

Three hundred hands unfolded. The six colossi, who had seemed to be nothing at all an instant before, now appeared in all their fabulous stature. I then formed in my throat the modulation which signifies: "It is the will of Uranus!"

The three hundred hands of the Hecatoncheires began to move in harmony, as if they were kneading the bread of the world or turning the wheel of the waters; and their one hundred and fifty heads drew together as if ready to hear and consider my commands. The eyes of the three Cyclopes, one blue, one yellow and one red, lit up the darkness, and a gentle warmth spread through the cavern.

Then I cried: "It is the will of Cronus!"

The hands began beating the air with a terrifying wildness; the eyes flashed lightning in all directions; there was an appalling smell of sulphur; the heat became intolerable; and the clamor was deafening even to a god. The walls of the anti-world shook as if they were about to collapse.

I quickly cried: "It is the will of Zeus!"

I felt a great relief on seeing the Hecatoncheires immediately fold their hands, the Cyclopes lower their lids, and all of them become absolutely still. It was, therefore, my turn to be their master, and I could control their strength for creation or destruction, or render them inactive.

I put my arm cautiously through the bars; I touched the colossi, even prodded them; and they did not move. They were as inoffensive as a club. I mean that a club is never dangerous in itself. Put it on the table, and it will stay there. What is dangerous is the will of the man who wields it, or simply the clumsiness with which he drops it on your toe.

I had, therefore, to be watchful of myself.

I began opening the padlocks. Not all ninety-six of them. I set about my work with considerable precaution. I limited myself to the first six, the top ones. It was enough.

A terrific push broke part of the door to pieces. The One-Eyed and the Hundred-Handed rushed through the breach. A brilliant flash of light brought me instantly to the surface of the world. I cried once again: "It is the will of Zeus!" to put a halt to their wild outburst, and my colossi gathered docilely at the mouth of a cave I showed them, by the sea.

I took my bearings, and realized that we had emerged in Sicily.

That beautiful, triangular island was still shaking on its foundations. The Hundred-Handed had raised a high mountain to provide themselves with an egress. From its yawning summit, crowned with glowing vapors, an incandescent earthen pulp was flowing, setting the trees on fire and engulfing all before it.

I congratulated myself on having opened only six padlocks. Had I opened them all, the shell of the terrestrial globe would no doubt have exploded.

In my desire to gauge the power of my new servants, I detached a fragment of rock and handed it to the red-eyed Cyclops. I saw the fragment melt and become transformed into lead. I took the lead and placed it in front of the yellow-eyed Cyclops; the lead was transformed into bright, silver pearls, which rolled in all directions. I recovered the quick-silver and placed it in the ray of the blue-eyed Cyclops. I watched the mercury change color, solidify and become gold.

Then I ordered the Hundred-Handed to beat the

sea along the shore, but each with only one hand. After a moment, I saw tiny green weeds appear on the surface of the waters; they closely resembled seaweed. But there I ceased my experiments. After all, the world had been made; and it seemed to me useless to waste my time remaking it, particularly at the risk of destroying it.

I had more urgent tasks.

Preparations for War.
The Helmet of Hades &
the Trident of Poseidon.
Iris the Messenger.

So I began to assemble my troops and organize them for battle. I had seen my brother Hades during my recent journey through the Infernal Regions, where he had remained concealed since being regurgitated from the entrails of Cronus. Dark Hades emerged by that same volcano of Etna which had served my own re-ascent.

I summoned my other brother Poseidon, who rose from the house of Oceanus in a great surging of seas.

I summoned my sisters Hestia, Demeter and Hera, who hurried to me from their various asylums. I asked Demeter to watch over the safeguarding of nature, the protection of vegetation, and the fecundity of species while the war lasted. I promised that the Seasons, the Hesperides, and even the Graces would shortly come to her assistance.

I made a pact with my uncle Oceanus, who was now no longer content with being a benevolent neutral, but declared himself my ally. He authorized me to make use of all his resources of which I might have need; and he promised to send help if I were in difficulties.

"I am confident I can keep Pontus and the furies of the seas quiet," he said. "Even better, I think I shall be able to persuade them to support you. I shall give no asylum to your enemies, and I shall drown them with terrifying storms if they ever drive you back to the frontiers of my shores."

He added, discreetly but clearly well informed: "I know my daughters wish you well. . . ."

I then had several secret conferences with my cousin Prudence. I made a point of showing her affection and gratitude, and of making it clear to her that I still thought of her with emotion. She, indeed, showed me some kindnesses in her own way which proved that she still felt tenderly towards me. And so it was at all our meetings. He is a lucky man who can make lasting friends of his first loves!

The river nymphs informed us that the Titans and giants were holding a line behind the high ranges that run from the Alps to the Caucasus. They were fortifying it. One could hear them at work beyond the summits, moving huge blocks of stone, piling up their projectiles; and when they exercised themselves for battle, their roaring breath bent the tops of the woods.

Having learned of Cronus's preparations, I ordered the One-Eyed to forge a helmet of black clouds which would make its wearer invisible. I gave this helmet to my brother Hades so that he could turn the enemy's flank without being seen and take him in the rear by surprise.

And I also asked the One-Eyed to use their collective strength to make a fork strong enough to open or raise mountains. I gave this trident to my brother Poseidon.

As for me, I made the Cyclopes gave me the fascicle of the javelins of the lightning.

I then arranged our order of march. The Hecatoncheires were to advance first, in a line, with their heads so turned that they would indicate to me the enemy's positions, and their hands ready to act. I would then follow, armed with the lightning. My daughter Athena would be at my side, holding Aegis, and ready to cover me. Poseidon would be slightly behind us, ready to support me and force breaches through which the secondary divinities, who had rallied to our cause, could advance. Finally, the heavy Cyclopes would follow and direct, on my orders, their destructive rays at long range.

Having made these dispositions and issued my orders, I sent to warn Themis to be ready to issue her decrees as soon as the victory was won, if it were won. If it were not, Memory would record a brave enterprise against tyranny.

To carry these messages I chose one of Oceanus's granddaughters, the beautiful Iris, a rapid traveler whose paths are the rainbows and who leaves behind her a shimmering wake. A rainbow, the passing of light through a shower, is always an omen. And Iris has remained the messenger of the gods.

I waited another of the world's nights so that Hades might circle round the Titan's defenses and take up his position in the vast, misty plains of the North.

When at last the chariot of the sun appeared in the sign foretold by the Destinies, I raised my shining right hand and cried: "Forward!"

The Battle Against
the Titans.
The Charge of the Centaurs.
The Treachery of Acheron.
The Ravages of
the Cyclopes.
Cronus Defeated.
The Titans Imprisoned
in Tartarus.
The Giants Pardoned.

Yes, it was a terrible war! The infinite sea roared, the Earth shook, the air was filled with an appalling clamor, and for days, which for you would be innumerable, the light was obscured by the smoke of conflagrations, while the nights were lit up by their flames. The elements confronted each other in fury and the glow of battle must have been visible from all the planets.

The Hecatoncheires went first into the assault, and one saw at once how strong their hands were. Three hundred hands tore the tops from the mountains; three hundred rocks poured down on the enemy. But the giants replied with equal vigor, and the blocks of stone they hurled fell all about us.

Poseidon broke through the skin of the Earth with his trident and opened huge breaches from which the water poured in cataracts. But the Titan Coeus, assisted by Alcyoneus and Porphyrian the red, immediately filled these crevasses with avalanches. The mountains changed their shape. Oh, how valorous Poseidon was! At one moment, Alcyoneus, the most outstanding of the giants because of his height, courage and strength, tried to seize his trident from him. They rolled on the ground in a furious hand-to-hand struggle, their limbs mingled, crushing everything beneath their weight.

Meanwhile, I had climbed the massif of Olympus from which Cronus had withdrawn. With one foot on Skolion, the other on Serai, and feeling these two pedestals quaking beneath me, I shouted my orders, sent the Hundred-Handed back into the attack, and brandished the lightning. Whenever I saw, through a gap in the clouds of dust, a Titan's shoulder rise above the summits, I loosed one of my fiery thunderbolts. The lightning flowed ceaselessly from my hand. They tell me I was magnificent.

It never occurred to me to take cover. But my dear Athena protected me. Holding Aegis in front of me, she warded off the innumerable rocks that were hurled at me. And with her spear she stopped charge after charge and onslaught after onslaught.

Down below, Oceanus and his sons were fighting an equally terrible battle against the monsters and furies engendered by Pontus, and the spray from their struggle rose up to us.

I saw Poseidon fighting under the huge Alcyoneus who was trying to strangle him. I hurled lightning at the giant who was blinded for a moment, let go his hold and fled, his hands over his eyes and his hair on fire. And Poseidon was able to recover his trident.

"Father!" Athena cried.

For behind me, both Porphyrion the red and the redoubtable Ophion, Eurynome's former husband, were advancing over the Pindus. Their chests were huge and hairy, and their legs so strong that the muscles swelled on them like snakes. I turned my thunderbolts on them. The hair of their bodies sizzled from head to toe. Porphyrion turned violet, while Ophion, to whom I had given good measure, rolled his burns on the ground uttering the most appalling roars. They were bald forever after, as were the crests of the Pindus which burned for several weeks.

At another moment, a rumbling almost as violent as my thunders shook both Earth and sky. "Has Cronus also got lightning?" I wondered anxiously as I heard the cyclone approaching.

It was the first centaur and all the race he had engendered coming down on us; their hooves raised whirlwinds of sand; and as they advanced they tore up the oaks and hurled them at us with their roots and branches. I stopped the centaurs' charge with my burning javelins; some reared up, others fell, beating the air with their six limbs as they tried, awkward and bewildered, to regain their feet; then they all retreated amid another thundering of whirlwinds to create panic and disorder in their own ranks.

By the next day they had reformed, and they returned; and this time, had it not been for the Hundred-Handed, who were drawn up in line behind huge ditches dug during the night, I doubt if I could have broken their charge.

And so it went—for many long days during which the black Erinnyes, their wings spread, and their hair full of blood, scoured the battlefield in all directions. At evening, the wind brought us by gusts the sour smell of the giants' sweat.

However, nymphs, fauns and even some sons and direct descendants of the Titans came under cover of darkness to enroll in our camp, which was continually increasing in numbers, so as to escape Cronus's oppression.

"But how comes it," I asked one morning, "that in spite of the defeats we inflict on them each day, our enemies constantly recover their energy and reappear to attack us with undiminished violence each dawn?"

"The fact is," my new allies informed me, "that the river Acheron, the Earth's son, is betraying you. Each night he gives the giants and centaurs to drink and thereby repairs their energies."

As a result, though I was somewhat anxious about loosing their terrible power, I decided to put the Cyclopes into the battle, for I realized there would otherwise be no end to it.

"Concentrate your forces and your fire on the Titans," I ordered them. "It is they, and above all

Cronus, who must be destroyed. Do not bother about the giants. They will surrender as soon as they see that their masters are defeated. It will be sufficient to make Acheron boil."

And, indeed, it did suffice. But at what a cost! Memory had warned me. He certainly boiled; but not only the water, for all else boiled too.

The Cyclopes were ready. The scarcely perceptible murmur they made when at rest had become a monstrous howling which drowned all other sounds. They bounded into the air, leaving a wake of fire behind them. They opened and closed their terrible eyes; and wherever the power flowing from their round eyeballs struck, everything was consumed in an intolerable incandescence. It was as if suns were born from the Earth, lasting only long enough to explode, immediately forming strange clouds that were at first wine-colored, then turned pink, then yellowish, then ashy pale; and these clouds rose, opened and fanned out, impalpable corpses of all living things floating on the currents of the ether.

The forests boiled; the soil boiled; sandstone and flint flowed like oil; marble turned to vapor.

Though surrounded by the breath of these furnaces and blinded by these braziers, Cronus and his allies continued to resist. The Titans Crios and Hyperion made a desperate effort to throw down on us whole mountain chains, and for a moment the Balkans trembled and the Caucasus were shaken. Meanwhile, Japetus and his son Atlas, clutching spread-eagled at the sky, were trying to detach pieces of it with which to crush us.

Forgetful of the past, they shouted: "Father, protect us!"

They were calling on Uranus to help them. But mutilated Uranus remained indifferent, mute and still. He left it to the Destinies to fulfill his vengeance.

Then Cronus was heard to cry: "Thanatos! Thanatos!"

Madman that he was, he wanted everything to be exterminated with him, if he were defeated. He was calling on the god of Death against the immortals themselves, against the elements, against the universe. He must have thought his prayer answered, for behind him there arose, as if come from the ends of the Earth, an invisible force, hidden in an impalpable fog as dark as night and as destructive as the fire of the Cyclopes, for everything became frozen and petrified as it advanced. The trees became rock; the metals contracted; quick-silver solidified; the very air, in the appalling cold, became hard as a knife.

It was my brother Hades, concealed beneath his black helmet, not the god of Death, but Hades the god controlling death, who was advancing for the ultimate assault.

Taken in rear, bewildered, pursued by this charge which had neither form nor visage, their bodies clasped in frozen arms they could not see, falling over each other as they tried to struggle free, the Titans finally collapsed, dragging Cronus with them in their fall, and came rolling to my feet.

On my orders, the Hundred-Handed immediately hurled themselves on them and secured them with chains.

I then stopped the fire of the Cyclopes, and I shouted to the giants: "Your masters are conquered and made prisoner! You can expect nothing more from them. Cease fighting, if you want to be spared!"

The giants were battered and weary; defeat weighed down their limbs. They hesitated a little; then Alcyoneus, Porphyrion the red, Ophion and all the rest let the rocks fall from their hands, and sadly bowed their heads. Athena forced them to their knees with her spear.

A great silence fell over the world, an impressive silence, in which each one, still incredulous that the war was over, could hear nothing but the sound of his own breathing. Then there soon arose a great clamor of joy. The victorious gods kissed each other and embraced. Nymphs and fauns surrounded them, leaping and dancing. Important and humble divinities came hurrying from every direction shouting their joy. The whole of creation, though exhausted and suffering from deep wounds, recovered its strength to celebrate its deliverance.

Yes, we had won; and we were happy!

Cronus was struggling in his bonds and they had to be doubled. The rogue was groaning and entreating me for mercy.

"Do not forget I am your father."

"I do not forget," I replied, "how you behaved towards yours. Do you remember the sickle?"

"Are you going to inflict the same treatment on me?"

"In view of what you normally do to your children," I said, "the gesture would not appear to have much importance nor to be much of a punishment."

"Where are you going to imprison me?"

"You will find out."

I assembled the One-Eyed and the Hundred-Handed.

"Cronus and his wicked brothers," I said, "will from now on occupy the prison to which Uranus in his wisdom confined them, and in which you were shut up by them for so long. The door will be closed. You will stand in front of it and be their jailers forever."

I repeated the phrase: "It is the will of Zeus!"

Then, with that wonderful and terrifying obedience which is theirs, the Hundred-Handed, without asking for any recompense, picked up the prisoners and carried them into the abyss. Cottos carried Crios and Hyperion over his shoulders; Gyges carried Colos and Japhet; and Briareus bore Cronus across his fifty necks. The Cyclopes, their eyes switched low and directed towards the depths of the world, escorted the procession. The last sight I had of my father was of his eyes filled with hatred and his cruel mouth with which he tried in passing to bite his brother Oceanus and his mother the Earth.

I made Atlas, Japetus's son, come forward.

"You tried to pull down the sky," I said. "From now on you will hold it up."

I sent for Acheron to appear before me.

"Son of Earth, you have given the enemies of light to drink; from now on you will flow beneath the Earth; your waters shall nourish the swamps of the Infernal Regions."

And I forgave the giants. I thought their mercenary forces could be recovered and that they might serve my reign as they had served my father's. As for the herd of centaurs, they had fled and disappeared into the sky of Asia.

My cousin Prudence—where had she been during the war, for I had not seen her?—then came up to me and said: "You are wrong to forgive the giants."

"Not at all," I replied. "See how humble they are, how sorry for themselves. They are not responsible. They obey whoever commands them. And I do not want to deprive myself of their strength for repairing the devastation."

"There is danger of their causing you a great deal of trouble."

But I was determined. It was my only mistake, and it proved costly. As a result of it, I had to fight another war ten years later.

"On the other hand," Prudence went on, "you have been wise in your treatment of Cronus and his brothers. The forces of the Cyclopes and the Hecatoncheires will find sufficient employment in keeping the forces of the Titans under control. Thus both sides will stay quiescent in the depths."

"From the point of view of our own safety," I said, "I would have preferred a less delicate balance of forces. For when you talk of a balance, you also imply the danger that it will not be maintained. But I could think of nothing better."

"All stability is a balance," Prudence replied. "It is up to you to see that it is maintained. For the moment, we are in no danger, for the universe is weary."

Night fell, a calm night without terror. How many years, how many eras was it since the Earth had known the cool of evening, the sweetness of peace? The last songs of the liberated divinities ceased as the stars began to shine again. Nature and the species could begin to plan and dream once more.

"I have conquered and I am happy!" I repeated to myself. But exhaustion prevented my enjoying the full savor of victory. I went to sleep, putting off till the morrow, when my mind would be rested, the solving of all the problems of which I was already aware.

The World After the War.
The Assembly of the Gods.
The Principle of Power.
The Election.

What desolation there was on my awakening! Though no continent had disappeared on this occasion, the regions in which the war had raged

presented a desperate sight. Several rivers had changed
their course owing to the Titans' fortifications. Their
waters had formed huge lakes on the summits of new
mountains, while ancient peaks had tumbled into the
sea. A stunted vegetation shivered on the crests, while
down below everything was scorched and turned to
ashes. Vast plains, which had been richly sown by the
hand of Uranus, had become deserts. Every species
had been sorely tried. Such men as had escaped
emerged fearfully from their caves, and in what condition! Haggard, naked, stunned and bewildered, they
trembled as they gazed at the livid clouds which, raised
by the battle, were now slowly dissipating in the sky.

"I have seen all this before, I have seen all this before," Memory kept saying.

The gods who had taken part in the war, and many
others whom I did not yet know, had joined me on
Olympus. They seemed to be scarcely less bewildered
than mankind. They all talked at once, congratulating
themselves on the success and recounting their exploits. The newly arrived, in particular, pressed themselves forward to surround my brothers and myself
and evince their gratitude, whether feigned or sincere;
they wanted to explain the reasons that had prevented
their joining us earlier, and some boasted of mysterious
feats of courage which, if they were to be believed,
had greatly helped to overthrow my father. But they
all showed anxiety about the future and were in considerable confusion.

How was power to be exercised under the new divine generation, and how was the world to be reor-

ganized? Where was each to be installed and what was to be his part in the work and the joys to come?

I avoided answering these questions, and still more giving orders.

Themis, as I had arranged with her, called for silence. The gods sat down in the great amphitheater formed by the mountains; it still smelt strongly of burning. And when they had all taken their places and were ready to listen, Themis spoke as follows:

"Our first act must be to give the supreme power to one among us. Indeed, our actions will be fruitless and ineffective unless they are complementary, unless each of us takes account of and derives assistance from the actions of his neighbor. And so that our actions may be complementary, it is necessary that they should form part of a concerted whole and a general plan; and to make such a plan possible, we must recognize an authority which can define it and see that it is obeyed; we must all relinquish a fraction of our individual power of decision and action, for our power will be sterile if we try to preserve it in its entirety, and we must set up a common directing *power*. We must therefore appoint a leader who will promulgate decrees, see to their execution, apportion tasks, prevent encroachments, arbitrate disputes, punish shortcomings, reward effort and prowess, and, in a word which sums up all the rest, reign over us and the world."

She fell silent.

Many of the gods looked at me. They had obeyed

me during the war and seemed surprised that I should not continue to command them. I said not a word.

"We must choose the strongest!" some cried.

"We must choose the wisest," others said.

"We must choose the oldest," the sons of Oceanus suggested.

At this moment a new divinity entered the assembly. Her beauty and the way she moved created a diversion. She came forward with a calm assurance, holding in her hand, as one might hold a flower, a branch of coral. She seemed to be admiring her reflection in the eyes of all.

"She is your aunt Aphrodite, Uranus's youngest daughter," Memory whispered to me.

Aphrodite seated herself, assuming an elegant pose. Her beauty was undoubtedly striking. Her silky hair had the undulations of the sea; her nails were mother of pearl. Exquisitely dressed from head to foot, suntanned and scented, she had come from Cyprus and her appearance contrasted with that of the other divinities who were still wearing the dust of battle. She smiled at me; she smiled at my brothers; she smiled at all the male gods. The goddesses were immediately jealous of her.

The sons of Oceanus, prompt to change their minds, were already saying: "We must choose the most beautiful."

Themis began to speak again.

"I see with satisfaction," she said, "that you are all agreed."

Serious though the debate was, many could not help laughing.

"I did not mean it as a joke," Themis went on calmly. "You are all in agreement as to the necessity of a principle of authority, and none of you contests our need to establish a power. You are merely hesitating or disagreeing as to who should exercise that power."

Then the defeated giants, who were penned at the foot of Olympus, began to grow excited and shout: "Let the richest be appointed!"

I got to my feet, incensed.

"Silence, you," I said. "It is enough that I have pardoned you. You have not yet been asked for your opinion. Otherwise, I can show you in what my hand is rich."

And I raised my right fist which still held the lightning. Then I sat down again to allow Themis to continue.

"The richest," she said, "can derive his fortune only from the spoliation of others and his power from their abasement. My brother, the hateful Cronus, wanted to be the richest; see how he reigned, what disasters he caused, and what hatreds he aroused! The most beautiful has not necessarily the best brain; too preoccupied with himself, he is not conditioned to think of others, and judges merit by the adulation lavished on him. The wisest may lack decision in seeing his orders carried out, for he understands every point of view too well. The strongest is inclined to trust too much to his strength, and to govern by compulsion without listening to the views of others."

The gods were perplexed and looked questioningly at each other.

It was then that the clever Prometheus, followed by the loutish Epimetheus, appeared. They were both sons of Japetus, one of the defeated Titans, and brothers of Atlas, whom I had punished. Epimetheus came forward awkwardly, twisting his fingers. But Prometheus had a noble assurance, and an intelligent and not unhandsome face; energy, dreams and ambition could be seen in his eyes. He had come to make his submission, but he did so with such pride that he might have been mistaken for a victor. I at once detected in this cousin-german a possible rival. We were of the same age and resembled each other in more ways than one. I felt a certain mistrust of him and at the same time a certain sympathy for him. These two emotions are not necessarily incompatible.

"I come in the name of men," he said. "They are suffering the greatest destitution and are very anxious about the future. I have listened to your debate, and I am wondering to whom I should make the submission of which I am the bearer. Should it be to the best speaker?" he added, turning to Themis.

It was a clever maneuver. He was making use of his surrender to take part in the discussion, and was already claiming the support of a following. His loutish brother nodded approval.

"If he supports the best speaker," Memory said to

me, "it means he really does come in the name of men."

Themis replied to Prometheus: "The best speaker has need of all her time to weigh her words. She can propose and announce, but she cannot act; it is not her task to act."

"And the oldest," my uncle Oceanus said, "wants only to rest. And the state of the world today requires not rest, but work and enterprise."

Oceanus spoke seated, shaking his great beard of foam. He went on: "But the oldest, having seen much, and reflected and compared, is qualified to give advice. I counsel the gods here assembled to choose my nephew Zeus for king. He has shown his strength in battle; he has shown forethought in the way he prepared for war, and authority in the way he directed it. He is showing wisdom at this moment in abstaining from giving you orders. He is old enough to consider his decisions, while still possessing the ardor of youth. I have reason to believe that his person is sufficiently pleasing to the goddesses. He has the necessary knowledge to talk sense. None of these qualities are wholly rare when considered separately. But their combination is rare, and it is this that makes the quality of a king. I propose that the noble Zeus become our king."

The secondary divinities, crowded on the tops of the slopes, were already getting ready to approve. I rose and cut short the acclamations. The gods have not forgotten the speech I made.

"The domination of a leader," I said, "is really desired only in times of confusion. Later, it becomes burdensome to many. Everything in the heritage that has fallen to our lot needs reconstructing. Before making your decision, you should know how I intend to govern, if you elect me. I shall assemble you frequently, as you are now, so that you may discuss the affairs of the world and tell each other of your difficulties, problems and wishes. Themis, on the basis of your debates, will draw up decrees which everyone will have to obey. Some of the more active among you will form a council about me. My orders cannot ever be to everyone's taste. I have not made use of my lightning to impose myself on you; but, once king, I assure you that I shall use it to restrain or punish anyone, whoever he may be, who tries to oppose the promulgated decisions; my anger will then be terrible; there is still room in Tartarus. Weigh these things well before deciding. Themis has told you that power consists of everyone relinquishing a portion of their own. But these relinquishments, if they are to be valid, must be based on reason and freely accepted. True power exists only by consent; all other power is hazardous. There is neither greatness nor safety in reigning over slaves. I therefore desire that consent should be expressed. Let those who wish me to rule pick up a white stone and place it in the helmet of Athena, the goddess of Reason. If someone other than myself seems to you more suitable, or believes himself to be so, nominate him, or let him nominate himself, and choose a stone of another color. And if he is elected by a larger number of stones, I promise to hand the lightning over to him and to obey him."

No other god came forward. I certainly saw gleams of envy in Aphrodite's and Prometheus's eyes. But the first had none of the qualities for wielding power, and the second was in no position to demand it. They realized they would have no votes but their own. Athena went along the rows with her gold helmet. Then she came and emptied it at Themis's feet. Every stone was white. It was thus that election by vote was invented, a process which has since been put to considerable use.

The gods at once rose to their feet and acclaimed me, adding to my name Zeus, which means day, or light, all the titles with which I have since been honored: Chastiser of the Wicked, Dispeller of Misfortune, Refuge of the Weak, the Poor, the Fugitives, and the Supplicants, Defender of Friendship, Guardian of Cities, Protector of Popular Assemblies.

And so, mortals my sons, as you see, I did not become king by hereditary succession, by conspiracy, or by force. I did not even want to derive my authority from claims based on the war and the victory.

He was a Greek poet, well versed in the history of the gods, who wrote: "The saviour of a city is not necessarily its ruler."

I am, as I wished to be, an elected sovereign, first among equals.

THE FIFTH EPOCH

The Right Deed

The First Decrees.
Appointment of Hades &
Organization of
the Infernal Regions.
Functions & Aptitudes.
The Possessions of Hades
the Rich.

I began immediately to organize the administration of the empire by delegating a part of my power to such gods as I considered the most diligent and the most sure.

To my brother Hades, I assigned the government of the Infernal Regions, charging him to keep an eye on Tartarus below and warn me of the slightest stirring there. He would also have to receive the dead and be responsible for the slow and secret mutations of their energies. To assist him, he would find there already the river-god Styx, the son of Oceanus and Tethys, whose meandering arms surrounded the infernal domain; Acheron, the prisoner, would carry out the more menial duties; and the old demon Charon, who had been put there by Uranus, as a punishment for some misdeed, would continue to ferry the dead.

Styx is terrifyingly silent and dark. Even Charon's boat can make no ripple or wake in those thick waters. The banks of Acheron are black, fetid mud, in which the bubbles rising from decomposing corpses are continuously bursting. Thick reeds conceal the approaches and anyone venturing into them sinks into the mud never to rise again.

You are no doubt thinking that Hades's portion is a melancholy one. Do not believe it, my sons. No one part of the world is more melancholy than another for him whom it suits. And Hades is half blind. He was born so. He cannot bear the light of day, and can see only in the dark. The helmet conferring invisibility I had ordered for him from the Cyclopes was not intended only to conceal him from the enemy, but also to protect him from the sun's rays. And when my cousin Prudence disappeared from the battlefield, it was, as I later learnt, to lead Hades by the hand to his attacking position. Imagine my brother's difficulties had I given him the government of the rising sun!

The Infernal Regions for you and me, who are lovers of the light, are an appalling place. But not for him. Each man may have a different hell.

Since every job in the world must be done, the Destinies, guiding Clotho's hand, cause her to draw certain numbers in the lottery which seem to you unfortunate or disastrous. You are surprised that there should be happy grave-diggers. And yet they exist. You are astonished that a man should make dissecting corpses his profession, and yet be a good companion at the dinner-table or an ardent lover in the bed. You believe that such duties, which are essential to the city, are always accompanied by a sort of mental infirmity in those who perform them. But genius, too, when you come to consider it, is always accompanied by some infirmity. You envy the elect of the Muses the position he occupies at the summit or at the limits of your species; but do you realize that the admiration you devote to him and the applause you give him reach him only through the bars of that solitariness which is his infirmity and without which he would not be what he is?

The important thing is to recognize early the state which best suits one's particular nature, and to do one's best to excel in it. I repeat: he who accepts his destiny is guided by the Destinies; he who rejects it is forcibly led.

To walk upright in a little shadow is often preferable to limping in the light. There is a perfect way of being a cobbler, as there is a detestable one of being a banker, a dancer, or a magistrate. And it is better to be an excellent grave-digger, and therefore a happy one, than to be a bad sculptor or an incompetent minister.

Among the labors of kings, not the least is to promulgate such laws as will permit each man to adopt the state which suits him best.

So do not pity Hades or think that he was hardly done by. Besides, he does not govern only the asylum of the dead. He also controls the strata of minerals and metals which the subterranean regions contain. That is why he is most often invoked under the name of

Pluto, which means the rich. Is not the possession of precious metals for many of you a pleasure, indeed a passion that comes before all else? Pluto rules over these hidden treasures and defends them jealously. For each portion abstracted from him, he demands an equal weight in lives, and compensates in one of his domains for what is taken from him in the other. Unfortunate miners on whom the mountain falls or who are drowned in the gallery they are working by some arm of the Styx, prospectors for gold whose bones whiten by sandy desert tracks, over-ambitious financiers whose exhausted hearts give way or, faced with ruin, cast themselves into the abyss, all these are the innocent or willing victims of Hades the Rich. And if the energy of the Cyclopes, whose guardianship I have given him, was liberated and destroyed his treasures, you may be sure that Pluto would abolish all life.

And remember also that Chance is a member of his family and, as he is, blind.

Establishment of Poseidon
the Unsatisfied.
The Nereids.
Amphitrite.
The Loves &
Children of Poseidon.
The Second Cyclopes.
Pegasus.
New Giants.
Orion.

Thus one of my brothers was provided for. Since my uncle Oceanus desired to rest, I appointed my other brother, Poseidon, to relieve him of his duties and take over the government of the seas.

Considering the extent of the sea, the forces which act on it, and the riches it contains, one cannot think that Poseidon was wronged. But my trident-bearer is turbulent by nature; had I left him on land, it would no doubt have quaked unceasingly. One has merely to see how he behaves towards the boundaries of his own domain! Coasts and shores suffer continuously from his activities. He will dry up or silt up a harbor, which was dredged with much effort, and which he used to favor by bringing abundance to it with the merchant fleets. And he will suddenly decide that a cliff, which for a thousand years has been the site of a prosperous city, blocks his view; he will sap it or knock it down without even sparing the temple dedicated to himself. Few islands have not reeled from his blows, few beaches have not been ravaged by the pranks of his furious flood tides. I restrain him as much as I can.

Dissatisfaction seems to be his lot, as it is that of the sailors who take to his waves. But nothing can be changed, created or discovered except by the impulsion, as eternal as the sea, of dissatisfaction.

Poseidon chose for wife one of the Nereids. We must say a word about them in passing; for the poets often mention them for the beauty of their hair, but without making it very clear who they are. Their father, old Nereus, is a very ancient god who, though the son of Pontus, has always shown kindness towards sailors. Through their mother, the charming Doris, the sister of Metis and Eurynome, they are descended from Oceanus. Age did not prevent Nereus from being fecund; there are seventy-seven Nereids. Sometimes they remain quietly sitting on golden thrones in the halls of their father's palace at the bottom of the sea, which is then as calm as a mill-pond. But they love to come to the surface to play, sing and frolic; they laugh and chase each other, roll over each other, break, and with their careless backs raise and toss the hulls of ships. It is their hair one sees shining under the moon.

Well, of these seventy-seven, Poseidon wanted Amphitrite, who did not want him. He had seen her dancing with her sisters on the shores of the island of Naxos. She was neither more beautiful nor gayer than the others, just a pretty wave, happy to leap and splash, roll in to break upon the shore and bound again. Anyway, such as she was, it was she who pleased him.

He approached her, trident in hand, and gauche from love. The other Nereids mocked. It is never good tactics to pay court to a girl among her companions. Poseidon tried to embrace Amphitrite; whether her modesty was real or feigned, or merely playful, she escaped him. In his irritation, he became violent; she took fright, and from then on he was odious to her. He tried to take her by force; she ran away; he pursued her; she fled far, far away, sometimes diving, sometimes surfacing again all disheveled, and disappeared towards the West. Poseidon organized a search for her. Currents, tides, winds, gulls, cormorants, mullets, tunny and eels, the whole marine world were called in to help. No quiet cockle or peaceful sponge was not alerted. If you are really determined, and prepared to take every possible step, it is possible to find a particular wave in the sea. But what advantage can be derived from such persistence? An escort of dolphins brought an exhausted and eternally hostile Amphitrite back from the Sargasso Sea. Poseidon united with her, but had no child by her.

Dissatisfaction! He sought diversion in other loves, which were all fecund; but Poseidon's children were all odd and often mischievous. Some, whom he had by Thoösa, Amphitrite's cousin, were born with a single eye in their foreheads or several arms at each shoulder. Whether it was a chance recurrence of Uranus's heredity, or whether it was deliberately intended, it fortunately so happened that Poseidon's Cyclopes had neither a tithe of the strength nor the docile intelligence of their predecessors.

Though huge, brutal and vicious, they were so stupid that they could be controlled easily enough, and even put to useful work. "Does your foot hurt you? Take a rock and crush it to punish it." It was with reasoning such as this that they could be kept quiet. Moreover, they were not immortal.

For a while, I placed them, under the direction of Prometheus, at the disposal of men, who were then laying the foundations of their cities. Men used these colossi to construct, in accordance with the techniques handed down from Atlantis, the walls and buildings you still call Cyclopean.

Then, one by one, Poseidon's Cyclopes died. The brave and ingenious Ulysses, so dear to my daughter Athena, and whose adventures you well know, defeated the last of them, the monster Polyphemus.

What strange passion was it that for a time drove my brother Poseidon into the arms of the Gorgon Medusa? By her he had Pegasus, the winged horse, whose hooves produced springs of water wherever they touched the ground; he was certainly beautiful to look on, but not very manageable and, one must admit, of very little use.

Of the same union, Chrysaor was born, the giant with the golden sword. Had they got on together, what terrible incursions they would have perpetrated,

Chrysaor mounted on Pegasus! But Pegasus refused to carry Chrysaor; and it was Bellerophon, another of Poseidon's sons, who mounted him, on my orders, to go and slay the Chimaera, after which, Pegasus insisted on flying so high that he reached the stars. I requested him to stay there.

As for Chrysaor, who was himself remarkably incompetent, he had a son called Geryon, a giant with three bodies joined at the hips, whom my son Heracles had difficulty in killing.

There was an endless succession of impossible variations, of delirious dreams, which were all too reminiscent of the follies of the Titans when they set about creating! I really cannot go into these obsessions.

By our sister Demeter, whom he loved—I shall soon have occasion to return to this—after I had loved her, Poseidon had, against the unfortunate goddess's will and at a most inappropriate time, another strange horse called Areion, and a daughter whom I decreed should never be named.

Poseidon's imagination was thoroughly roused one day when he saw the beautiful mortal, Iphimedeia, of Prometheus's line, walking naked along the beach and, somewhat provocatively I must admit, amusing herself by cupping water in the palms of her hands and trickling it over her breasts! Oh, take care, you bathing girls!

Poseidon had two sons by Iphimedeia; they were monsters and each year grew a cubit taller and a fathom in girth. These two strapping fellows, by name Otus and Ephialtes, were tiresome, conceited, turbulent and aggressive; at the age of nine they joined the defeated giants and took part in their rebellion. It was they who tried to pile Pelion on Ossa. But their misdeeds were not limited to these; they confined my son Ares in a bronze pot for thirteen months, and made outrageous advances to the goddesses on Olympus. When my punishment eventually overtook them, they were not spared.

But do you imagine this is the end of the list? It certainly is not.

Cercyon and Sciron, two frightful brigands, who spread terror for a long while, one near Elusis, and the other near Megara, by ransoming and killing travelers, were also sons of my brother. It was the excellent Theseus who freed the country of these two scourges. But, no doubt so that such a splendid race should not die out, Poseidon made Alope, Cercyon's daughter and his own granddaughter, pregnant.

And must we recall his deplorable love affair with Halia the Telchine? The Telchines, marine demons who haunted the neighborhood of Rhodes, had harbored and protected Poseidon during our dangerous youth, as the Curetes had protected me in Crete. And their sister, the beautiful Halia, the divinity of Salt, had been to my brother very much what Amaltheia had been to me. What uneasy nostalgia and what memories of unassuaged adolescent desire drove Poseidon to seeing Halia again? Some people would have been content with merely talking of the past. But from this meeting Halia bore six sons, six scapegraces who, as soon as they had reached puberty, agreed among themselves to rape their mother in turn. Less indulgent to other people's faults than to his own, Poseidon pursued his six sons with blows from his trident and, opening up the bottom of the sea, engulfed them. Halia had demanded no such vengeance. Crushed by so many undeserved misfortunes, she sank into the depths of the sea and never reappeared.

Of all Poseidon's children the only one of any interest, and I regret him, was Orion the hunter, a young giant who walked on the waves, and was so handsome that Aurora herself fell in love with him. Every morning she enveloped him in her rays as he went from Delos to Mykonos, his head high and his bow over his shoulder. But Orion, like his father, was fated to have an unfortunate love. His career was short. Though he could have had almost any goddess he wanted, it was my daughter Artemis, the most refractory in love, whom he sought. Without deluding myself overmuch, I looked on the affair with approval; they had in common a passion for hunting. But instead of pursuing Artemis, admiring her and serving her, Orion set her at defiance, which was stupid of him. And, which was even less adroit, he tried to take her by force. Proud Artemis was so angry that she made a scorpion sting Orion in the heel. Then she sent both of them to join the constellations. None is more beautiful than Orion; three stars twinkle at his golden belt. But Orion flees from the summer sky when the Scorpion appears, protecting the Virgin's advance.

Indeed, my brother Poseidon has not been wholly a joy to me. But the ever-shifting realm I gave him was the most suited to his unstable and contrary nature; anywhere else, he would have caused me more anxiety.

First Labors; First Sowings.
The Requests of Prometheus.
Rhea's Visit.

And I reserved for myself the direct government of the earth and the air. I soon discovered the difficulties of being a king. From all sides, the gods of the soil, of animals and of plants turned to me, seeking orders, laws and directives. Above all, they expected recipes for happiness, as if a change of reign must bring immediate relief to their ancient ills, and as if my intervention could procure everyone complete and immediate felicity.

My cousin Prometheus kept petitioning me. A tardy adherent, he became particularly harassing.

"Man, think of man," he kept saying. "His present condition is unworthy of both him and us. Something must be done for man at once."

What promises had he made to be so insistent in his demands?

"No one is more concerned about man's condition than I am," I replied. "But what is the use of endowing

him with the powers you demand before we have
healed the wounds of the soil and repaired the ravages?
What happiness can man find in those unhealthy forests
and those scorched pastures? Sickles, sickles! Of course,
we shall give him sickles. But first there must be a
harvest. And for there to be a harvest, there must be
a sowing. Otherwise sickles will merely enable men
to mutilate each other. My sister Demeter will start
by teaching them which grains are useful to them."

I worked as hard as I could, went from one region
to another, and kept the Seasons, the river-gods and the
nymphs of the fields up to their work. The Earth soon
became a great humming work-yard, as it must have
been during Uranus's reign. All the natural forces took
part in the work; and even impatient Prometheus had
to agree that there was an improvement.

But as the task progressed, I realized how immense
it was, and at times wondered whether I should ever
be able to complete it. The gods and the species considered me decisive and assured; they believed my
energy inexhaustible. No one, apart from my sisters,
could imagine the anxiety that often assailed me. For
every evening, feeling harassed, I would join my three
sisters, the only goddesses to whom at that time I
wished to unburden myself of my anxieties, admit my
fears or reveal my weariness; their company gave me
that feeling of family security of which my childhood
had been deprived.

But you are no doubt wondering what had become
of my mother Rhea of the beautiful hair. Had I seen
her, and why was she not living with me?

I had, of course, got to know my mother; it had been my first wish. As soon as I had been elected, I had sent an escort of nymphs to meet her and conduct her to Olympus. My eyes had at last been able to contemplate her sublime face, which was marked with sorrow, and her abundant, but now silvering, hair. We had talked for a long while, and had not understood each other.

My mother lived by three prides and three misfortunes. Her prides were that she was a daughter of a king of the gods, the wife of a king of the gods, and the mother of a king of the gods. Her misfortunes were to have seen her father mutilated, her husband in chains, and her children devoured.

"But since, thanks to your subterfuge, I was saved, and all your other children have now returned to the light of day, be happy," I said.

"Nothing can efface the past," she replied. "Nothing can make up for the fact that I could not bring you up, or that I was deprived of your first smiles and of those of your brothers."

"But we have now all come together again!"

"Is it not a grief the more to have come together so late, when we should never have been parted?"

I realized she was the goddess of Regret.

She regretted everything. She retained a nostalgia for her wonderful childhood in the gardens of Atlantis; she sighed complacently over the follies of her youth; she lamented her disastrous marriage; and she moaned about her sad life as wife and mother. And now something in her nature led her even to regret Cronus; or, rather, she regretted that Cronus had not been other than he was.

She did not seem to feel any satisfaction at my victory, except in the presence of the other divinities. "Look," she seemed to be saying, "what a powerful god I gave birth to!" But to me she said: "How can I rejoice that my son has been obliged to overthrow his father for the salvation of the world?"

She did not want it ever to be forgotten that her life had been one long succession of unparalleled sufferings.

"Mother," I asked her, "where do you want to live?"

"In Crete," she replied.

I showed surprise at her choice, and she seemed vexed by my surprise.

"Was it not there I brought you into the world, and thereby gave you your future kingdom? Was it not there I accomplished the most important work of all for the future of the universe?"

"You shall reside in Crete, mother, and you will be honored there."

Just before leaving, Rhea remembered that she had granddaughters and wished to meet them. I immediately summoned the Muses, the Fates, the Graces and all my female children to introduce them to her.

"This is Athena, my eldest, the daughter of Metis; these are Memory's daughters. . . ."

Rhea smiled sadly at each of them.

"I do not suppose," she said, "that these children will come to see me very often. It is quite understandable, of course, for they all have their work to do. But is it not sad to have to live all alone when one has so many grandchildren?"

I did not point out that she had chosen her place of residence herself; nor, on the other hand, did I suggest she should alter a decision she already regretted. Before showing myself a good son, I had to take care to show myself a good king. And my mother, abusing the respect she invariably inspired, would have paralyzed the council of the gods by talking entirely of herself.

The nymphs, to whom I added dolphins and tritons, formed the escort which took her to Crete. Since then, her days have been spent in quietude. Amaltheia is her principal companion, and their memories form the constant basis of their conversation. For memories are like food which can be prepared in twenty different ways; and thus one always eats the same foods, though varying their appearance, spicing and taste.

My mother discourses to travelers at length about her loneliness and my exploits. Pious men have raised many temples to her, and women everywhere celebrate her cult.

One day, to my surprise, I found myself saying: "I really regret that my mother's character is as it is. . . ."

I at once broke off and asked my daughters to tell me if I ever began to resemble my mother Rhea.

*Hestia, the Goddess
of the Hearth.
The Functions of Virgins.*

It was my sister Hestia who took over the running of my house.

Hestia, the eldest of the six of us, hates traveling and fears all adventure, even that of love. She is content only with sameness, and will dislike tomorrow if it does not resemble today. When our brother Poseidon, whose disappointments had by now become innumerable, at one time took it into his head to pay court to Hestia, she was terrified at the thought of changing her condition, and implored me to authorize her to preserve an eternal virginity. And this I gladly granted her since, in her present state, she rendered me invaluable services, but did not inspire me with desire.

It was not that she was ugly. Indeed, Hestia is beautiful, but her beauty is of the placid, regular kind, which is apt to pass unnoticed. Her perfections lack radiance.

It is wives who make the home; mistresses upset it; and daughters, when their turn comes to be mothers, desert it. Each one, by lighting a flame on her own hearth, puts out another; and they all, on becoming grandmothers, shiver in front of the cold ashes. Only the virgin has permanence.

Happy is the house in which a virgin without fancies, born for devotion, sees to it that everything is in its place, that customs are respected, and each evening puts a log on the fire with the same gesture. It is then that the generations stay round the hearth.

It is because the fire continues to burn that the fickle husband comes home; it is in front of this fire, which has cast its light on so many shared days, that the guilty wife is forgiven; and it is by this warmth that the sons-in-law come to sit, and the errant son, entering silently, and the young widow holding her children by the hand.

The guardian virgin, with her intact body, does not live for herself; her emotions are nourished only by the joys and sufferings of others. She is the confidante of the adolescent's angers; and the old man is not ashamed to admit to her that, in his heart of hearts, he feels like the child he once was.

Because she has never given birth, time seems to have stopped for the guardian virgin; and she spreads the illusion that the dead are merely absent.

I have often reminded my sons and daughters of what they owe to my eldest sister. She allots their tasks to the serving nymphs, superintends the ordering of processions and feasts, and urges on the Seasons, when they are lazy of a morning, to harness the chariot of the sun. Without her, without aunt Hestia as she is called, Olympus would certainly not be the big busy household it is, but merely a tribunal in which I would sit on a cold throne.

I have ordained that the cult of Hestia should be observed in all the houses of men, and that her statue be placed in all the temples of all the gods. But these statues are like Hestia herself in that one often passes them without noticing them.

Demeter.
Her Joys & Her Labors.
The Gardens of the Seine.
The Clock of the Flowers.
Philadelphianism.

Unlike Hestia, who cares for nothing but her home and never sets foot beyond the palace courtyard, my sister Demeter is happy only in the orchards and fields. I have often gone out to look for her at night, when anxious that she has not come home, and have found her clothed only in moonlight, her ear pressed against a tree and her arms encircling it.

"I am listening to the sap," she would explain.

The scent of mown hay has always thrown her into an ecstasy, and even the sickly smell of rotting leaves intoxicates her. I have often seen her plunge her long white hands into black humus, knead the soil, and breathe its odor.

"This is tomorrow's life," she would say.

She has only to take a fruit in her hands and it will bring forth yet larger ones.

She thought the corymb of the flowers of the white-beam too thick on the stalk. "So many hopes clustered in the same stalk are bound to give poor fruit," she decided. From the whitebeam she derived the wild cherry, still sour but with more flesh, then the fine fat cherry, rich and sweet, with its blood-red skin, as well as the big bigaroon your children eat on their way to school.

And the gourds! Demeter devoted herself to gourds. I remember her laughter and happiness that summer's day when she brought the first gourd to the table of the gods, carrying it as if she had plucked the sun. She was indeed Uranus's granddaughter! One could see in her, as in each one of us, some characteristic of the founder demiurge. To Poseidon fell his unceasing and turbulent imagination, to Hades the energy for slowly maturing plans, and to me the capacity to preserve a balance, to coordinate these various forces, and to be the principle of organizing and directing sovereignty.

During this first period of my reign when I was more occupied with reorganization than creation, and when the most urgent task was to reimpose order on nature, my sister Demeter was my companion, my colleague and my mistress. Together we would set off to labor in the divine work-yards. The terraces of Tuscany, the orchards of Umbria, the huertas of Iberia, the palm-groves of Ifrikia and the green valleys of the Lebanon are all lands that preserve the memory of our labors.

I want to linger for a moment on a happy episode. It was when we were staying with our relative the river-god of the Seine. The rich harvests of that basin are clear proof that we passed that way. Later on, men raised a column to my glory on the island of Lutèce; and they also dedicated a temple to me not far away on a hill on the north bank.

Temple and column have disappeared beneath the foundations of other basilicas. My name, however, has remained attached to the height on which my temple stood; Mount Jove has become "Montjoie"; and for a long time kings used it as a battle-cry to rally the courage of their armies.

While sojourning among the gardens of the Seine, I was surprised to find that Demeter always rose before dawn.

"It is to watch the flowers opening," she said, "for they do not all open at the same hour and I should miss the earlier ones if I was not up before light. The first to open, when the night is still dark, is the white convolvulus. Then the poppy spreads its petals in the grey light of dawn. The blue-eyed flax follows shortly after; then the pimpernel and the golden-haired marigold. And so it goes from flower to flower till evening. And do not imagine that the mirabilis, the "beauty-of-the-night," is the last. When all else is asleep, the red convolvulus is open to close the circle. The flowers of this country, my brother, are truly a clock.

161

You men, who resemble me, must know that there are two kinds of sisters; there are those, such as Hestia, who as far as we are concerned are completely excluded from desire, so that the mere thought of uniting with them revolts us as an impiety; and those, on the other hand, with whom love seems to us to be the most natural, the most slaking, the most necessary and almost the most sacred of acts.

No mistress can be closer to us than a sister-mistress. No false modesty, that is to say no fear of not being accepted as we are, separates us from her, or her from us. One has no need to force the pace to discover her or make oneself known to her; it is oneself one finds, oneself one encounters in her arms. The sister who clasps her brother to her is in search of the strength of the father who engendered them. The brother, on his sister's breast, is in search of the mysterious night of the maternal womb. Together, they return to their origins and aspire to form again the couple their parents were.

Come on, my sons, be honest! Who among you has not dreamed of this particular purity, of this return to the fierce instant of his own conception? And how many among you who have had no sister, or no sisters you could desire, have not felt always a little frustrated by life? Do not indignantly refuse to admit it.

The son who unites with his mother is guilty of incest, for he is usurping his father's place and introducing disorder into the law of the continuity of the generations. Consider the punishment inflicted on Œdipus, even though he was driven to his misfortunes in spite of himself, and let him be a warning to you forever! But I have not condemned unions between brother and sister; you have made a crime of them of your own accord. Indeed, you must know that my priests have often blessed dynasties which practiced philadelphianism, and you should try to understand why I reserved such important destinies for the Ptolemies, Cleopatra and Berenice.

Well, these things began to become clear to me on the day when Demeter, making use of the same gesture with which she embraced trees, put her arms round me and her ear against my chest.

For anyone who likes luxuriant beauty, Demeter is certainly the most beautiful of all the goddesses. Her glorious hips are supported by strong legs. When she walks, two dimples smile in the supple hollows of her loins. Her curved stomach is smooth as marble; her breasts are generous and firm, her teeth brilliant, and her eyes large and blue. Her cheeks have the freshness of rose-mallows, and when she raises her thick, golden hair with both hands, one might think she was carrying on her head a rich sheaf from the first harvest. At least, this was how she looked throughout the year, before her misfortunes.

For our joys last but a short while. Demeter is first and foremost a mother rather than a mistress.

We had one daughter. Demeter, whose mind is uncomplicated, called her Kore, which simply means "the maiden." But Kore was soon to change her name and become Persephone. You all know that Persephone was carried off. But why and how did it happen? If any of you once knew, I wager he has forgotten. Anyway, this is the moment to tell you the true story, which is not one of the happiest of my reign.

Kore.
Her Youth & Abduction.
Hades's Brutality.
The Nymph Cyane.

One might have thought, from seeing her mother, that Kore would be the strongest and happiest of all my daughters. In fact, she was a pale, listless goddess with neither appetite nor gayety. As a child, she never played, shouted or laughed, and stared at the world about her with a disquietingly adult melancholy. Then she became a tall adolescent with pellucid cheeks and silky hair, who walked slowly through the fields of flowers. Her overabundant bosom, the only characteristic she had inherited from Demeter, seemed to weigh down her white shoulders.

I had asked Athena to educate her; but Kore showed more inclination for vague reveries than for study. I appointed several nymphs to accompany and amuse her, but she became friendly only with the nymph

Cyane, who resembled her. Kore liked Sicily, or rather she disliked Sicily less than anywhere else.

One night my brother Hades saw her lying asleep at the foot of a cypress. Oh, you young girls, who sometimes experience a contempt for life, remember that the hours of the night, when Hades emerges from his dark domain for a breath of air on earth, are dangerous!

As soon as he saw Kore lying there as still as if in death, Hades knew that he could never forget the sight of her. He hurried off to ask me for my daughter's hand. Is this the sort of request to make in the middle of the night? My damned brother woke me up!

I must admit that I replied rather casually. But at that particular time my mind was full of anxieties which pursued me even in my sleep. Several rivers I had had dug by the giants in the north of the African continent had disappeared into the sands and could not be found. Prudence suspected the giants of being responsible for this misdeed; she told me that they deliberately carried out their tasks badly, and that they exchanged mysterious messages. I was also anxious about what Prometheus was trying to do by continuously rubbing two pieces of wood together.

Kore herself was also an anxiety to me. It is a burden on a family to have a daughter who cares for nothing, desires nothing and does nothing. And here was an establishment, a husband and a kingdom for her.

The morbid languor of adolescent girls is often due to an excessive conceit of themselves; if they cannot be queens, they wish to be nothing. Kore, who had no employment on the Earth, might well find happiness as sovereign of the Infernal Regions.

Moreover, at that difficult time, I did not want to alienate a brother whose help in the war had been decisive, and who was now displaying, in his somber impatience, all the signs of violent passion.

"You want Kore?" I said. "Very well, take her."

And I went to sleep again.

I made a great mistake in omitting to tell Demeter.

The next day, at sunset, Kore was picking wild lilies on the heights of Enna.

Do you know Enna, in the heart of Sicily? Have you ever walked its steep lanes in the blue dusk, amid the unyoked, sidling oxen, and the herds of goats with long brown horns being driven to the folds? It is the hour when the women in black veils go into the temples and, group by group, kiss the feet of the statues. Have you ever heard these women chanting before the altars their eternal laments for the sufferings of life and the horror of death?

Well, Kore was picking lilies.

Hades, who had spent the day hiding in some crevice on Etna, three divine paces away, seized her and abducted her. He was wearing the helmet that made him invisible to the world.

I had never imagined that the silly fellow would take my reply literally and behave in this way. A few well-turned compliments and prettily phrased vows would have been just as effective as violence.

Clasped in his invisible arms, Kore uttered a scream of terror and the mountain long reverberated to its echo.

Seeing her companion being dragged away, the nymph Cyane dashed over the hills to rescue her. But who can battle with the god of the Dead when he has seized his chosen prey?

In his fury, Hades struck the nymph and changed her into a spring at that very place, near the gulf of Syracuse, where he opened the abyss by which he dragged Kore down into the entrails of the Earth.

The spring Cyane resembles no other. It forms a huge, perfectly circular basin filled with dark, freezing water. Women, I advise you not to bathe in it! You cannot see its bottom; indeed, you will see nothing but your own reflection, obscured, quivering, and as if half effaced from life. Do not stay too long gazing into this mirror; it is one of the entrances to the Styx and one can see that it was at this place Hades made his descent.

Her head and shoulders emerging from this pit to which she is bound by the waist, the beautiful Cyane, forever disconsolate, weeps upon the ground. Her long thick, soft hair of weeds spreads down to the sea, and her liquid arms encircle shady islands where the lovers of Syracuse come to exchange their first kisses.

It is a mysterious river, constantly watched over by a sparrow-hawk hanging motionless in the sky; tall papyri, unusual in this part of the world, grow on its banks, and are proof of some secret link with the Nile, as was the tree, rather like a pomegranate, which then grew there, and of which Hades plucked the fruit before he disappeared.

Demeter's Despair.
Poseidon Pursues Her.
The Horse Areion &
the Sterile Lady.

At this time Demeter happened to be in Egypt where she was kneading the alluvium so that it might produce several harvests a year. She heard her daughter's scream, and her heart was frozen with anguish.

She stood up, abandoning her task, and hurried to Sicily, where she could find no trace of her child. She hastily made her way to Olympus; all out of breath, she seized my hands and asked me where Kore was.

Like a coward, I replied I did not know.

Throwing the veil of a dark cloud about her shoulders, she set off at hazard, like some great mad bird. For nine whole days and nights, without washing, attiring herself or doing her hair, without taking food or rest, she scoured the whole Earth and flew over the seas, ceaselessly calling her daughter, and demanding the whereabouts of her darling Kore from every mountain and river, and from every god she met.

She carried a lighted torch in each hand and her mind was so distracted that she forgot to extinguish them during the day.

My brother Poseidon, as I have already told you, had desired Demeter ever since he had learned that she had loved me. Now that he heard her lamenting along the shores, he thought his hour had come.

He approached our sister, pretended to wish to console her and, on the first beach they came to, tried to take advantage of her distress.

This was not at all the sort of consolation Demeter wanted. She was indignant, struggled, drove him off and, her body covered with sand and her eyes filled with tears, she got to her feet to continue her demented quest. But Poseidon pursued her; they both hastened across the world, one driven on by sorrow, the other by desire. They crossed straits, deltas and peninsulas; capes and cliffs trembled at their passing.

There was a herd of horses grazing in Arcadia. Demeter, who was utterly exhausted, changed herself into a mare for concealment and joined the herd. But Poseidon, who was close on her heels, noticed the white mare, which was taller, more beautiful and had a larger crupper than the rest; moreover, its nostrils were steaming and its limbs trembling as if from a long race. He discerned the trick and immediately changed his shape too.

As a goddess, Demeter had resisted the assaults of the god; as a mare she had to submit to those of the stallion.

From this loveless union, consummated due to lassitude, and in all the brutality of animal desire, two strange beings were born, one misfortunate, the other maleficent.

Areion, the horse that talks, is the misfortunate one; on the offside he has human feet instead of hooves. Horses keep clear of him, and men, though he has rendered them services by his speed and ability, continue to treat him as a horse.

The maleficent one is that daughter whom I refused to allow to be named, so that it is impossible to invoke her. She is simply known as the Lady, or the Mistress, or again as "she who must not be named." She comes towards you without seeing you, for she is blind. At her passing, fruits wither on the trees, flowers fade, and children die in women's wombs. Thus the Lady avenges herself for her sad birth and for her mother who abandoned her.

For as soon as Demeter had given birth among the herd, she resumed her former shape; she picked up her torches and continued her search for Kore.

On the tenth day, she met Hecate and questioned her.

Hecate & Magic.

I have not yet told you about Hecate, the daughter of Perses and Asteria, who were themselves children of the Titans. She exercised important functions even before my reign began. Far from opposing my accession, she predicted and supported it; she was one of the most active of those unknown allies who prepared the world for my victory. I confirmed her in the powers she had held from very ancient times in the universe, and even increased them.

The goddess Hecate has three bodies. When she walks clasping her hands, her arms form a garland about her; six legs surround the stone on which she sits; she is constantly looking in three directions at once, and one cannot look at her from behind.

You will, of course, have understood, since you are so quick, that thanks to her three bodies Hecate has the faculty of seeing simultaneously the past, the present and the future. And you will, of course, have been quite right; but do not be too hasty in congratulating yourselves. Remember that no first explanation is ever sufficient, and that every apparent meaning conceals another and more secret one.

Hecate is the goddess who is aware at one and the same time of the three aspects of a single object, its principle, its manifestation and its absence.

She is the goddess of Magic.

For preference she stands at crossroads, waiting to be consulted, for it is where roads cross and the judgment hesitates before which to take that it is most necessary to consult her. Mages, magicians and sorcerers, who are of her kinship, come at night to bring her their offerings and assemble about her for instruction. She is in communication both with the Infernal Regions and with the Uncreated. She does not change Destinies, but she can foresee them and assist their fulfilment. Circe the enchantress is Hecate's daughter. I have certain memories of beautiful Circe who put the art of magic to the service of love.

Hecate, whatever you may think, is a beneficent goddess. She inspires the orator at the tribune and the captain on the battlefield, if they have had the wisdom to consult her; she will also make the shepherd's flock prosper, fill the merchant's coffers with gold and the most humble fisherman's net with fish.

One may be surprised that she should afford her protection indifferently to the most diverse people and pursuits.

The fact is that magic is the science of the right deed at the right time, in the right place.

I repeat: magic is the science of the right deed, at the right time, in the right place.

I repeat once more: the science of the right deed, at the right time, in the right place.

All right! You heard me the first time. Thank me, all the same, for having repeated it three times.

Hecate is not concerned with your hierarchies; she knows that each action has the same weight, the same gravity, proportionally to each of your destinies, and that it is equally important to the fisherman to sail his boat to good waters at the right hour, as it is to the statesman to make the speech that will alter the history of his people at the right moment and in the right city.

But the man who is to do the *deed* rarely possesses the discernment necessary to choosing the *moment*, for this discernment requires a detached outlook which can take account both of the past and the future. Many a battle has been lost because an attack was mounted too hastily or postponed too long; and many a work has failed through impatience to undertake it or slowness to complete it. And how many opportunities for triumph or happiness have been missed for lack of knowing the right action to take!

The just appreciation of the *place* is perhaps even more difficult, for it requires a knowledge of the secret relationships between human temperaments and the components of a locality, between the action to be taken and the particular rhythms of expansion and decline which affect every country, from the vastest empire to the smallest terrain.

It is in all this that Hecate, the greater reader of the cosmic clock, can enlighten and assist you.

And even certain of her enchantments, which you curse because they inhibit your strength and your will, are sometimes salutary; in spite of yourselves, they prevent your acting at the wrong moment and oblige you to wait for the auspicious hour.

Demeter, therefore, questioned Hecate. And since Hecate, when consulted, raises two torches in those of her hands that are turned towards the present, Demeter thought at first that she was approaching a looking-glass.

Hecate, though she knew where Kore was, did not tell Demeter; but she advised her to go and ask the question of Helios, the Sun. For this is what good magicians do: rather than give you a direct answer, they prefer to put you in the way of finding it for yourselves.

Demeter Questions the Sun.
The Stone of Unhappiness.
Demeter Harbored by
the King of Eleusis.
The Kykeon.
The Kings of That Time.

Demeter immediately rose into the sky and hurried to the ardent Sun. Recognizing her as the great goddess she was, the Sun invited her to mount beside him in his chariot from which he sees everything. And there, while driving his flaming horses, he revealed to her where Kore was and by whom she had been abducted. He also told her that Kore, on going down to the Infernal Regions, had lost her name.

"But how did it happen that Zeus, her father and the king of the gods, did not prevent the abduction and has not even been told of it?" Demeter asked.

"Your brother Zeus has lied to you," the Sun replied. "He knows everything since he is Hades's accomplice; he gave him your daughter himself."

Oh, I told you, mortals my sons, that this episode does not redound to my glory! Let it at least serve to enlighten you and teach you that even the being whom everyone recognizes to be the most powerful is never wholly safe from committing an act of cowardice. For to lie is to fear; to lie is an act of weakness, and the consequences of telling a lie are nearly always worse than those of being frank.

The Sun's words crowned Demeter's anguish and finally destroyed her reason. She let herself fall from the flaming chariot and returned to Earth, though she refused to resume her place on Olympus. I sent Iris the messenger to her in vain; even the most beautiful rainbows could not persuade Demeter to do other than shake her head and refused to answer. I went to her myself, to try to justify myself and bring her back to us. She appeared not to recognize me and, for my part, I almost doubted whether it were really she, so greatly had misfortune and madness changed her.

The tall, happy, active Demeter, my dear sister with her round, laughing cheeks, her strong limbs and abundant bosom, had turned into an old woman half clothed in rags, sitting near Eleusis on a stone which has been known ever since as the "Stone of Unhappiness." Her hair hung down, dull and tangled; tears had furrowed her face; her breasts were like empty goat's skins on the trellis of her fleshless ribs. She could no longer remember, indeed she had no wish to remember, the children she had borne to Poseidon.

"Kore! Kore!" she groaned. And since "Kore," as I have told you, means "the maiden," all the virgins stopped before her. Among them were the three daughters of King Celeus who happened to be passing that way. When Demeter saw them looking so young and beautiful, carrying bunches of wild lilies, she burst into tears. The king's daughters took pity on the poor woman who seemed not to know even where she came from, and whose replies to their questions made little sense.

"My daughter has lost her name. . . . I have fallen from the chariot of light. . . . I am seeking an asylum. I want nothing but a humble servant's place."

The girls offered her shelter. But when Demeter entered King Celeus's house, they saw with astonishment that her head touched the joists, and that the door behind her had begun to shine with a golden radiance. They then began to think she was some supernatural being.

Since she refused either to sit down or to eat the food they gave her, a toothless old woman called

Iobe, who was sitting by the hearth, cried to her:
"Whoever you may be, beggar or goddess, if the
soup we eat here isn't to your taste, you know what
to do with it!"

And she accompanied her words with an obscene
gesture which unexpectedly made Demeter laugh. The
gods, and kings too for that matter, are not used to
being spoken to in this way, and a little downright
coarseness sometimes amuses them.

Demeter then drank the kykeon, a soup made of
barley gruel, milk, honey, fennel, mint and cummin,
which is still the drink given to new initiates at the
celebration of the mysteries. I have named the in-
gredients; but I shall not give you the recipe. This
is no ordinary piece of cookery that anyone can prepare at the corner of his stove.

Some of those who have told you the story of
Demeter may have given you the impression that
King Celeus was only a poor goatherd, and his palace
a miserable hovel.

The fact is that ten goats, a fire and a roof then
constituted the enviable lot of kings. Three beams
across the ceiling and it was a palace! These were
the signs by which one recognized princes.

Each of you who today possesses leather shoes,
linen and woollen clothes, a clock to tell you the
time, a cupboard in which drinks keep cool, an oven
from which food comes hot, two springs from which
gush boiling or iced water, and a powerful chariot to
take you from place to place, is a hundred times
richer than the richest king of ancient times. But he

is also, I hope, but a poor man as compared with tomorrow.

Demeter, the Child
& the Fire.
Triptolemus's Windmill.
The Sterile Year.

Demeter, however, insisted on being a servant. And as Metaneira, Celeus's wife, had just had a son, Demeter asked that he should be placed in her care.

But she was a strange nurse. Instead of feeding the child, she blew upon him and, when the household had gone to bed, she put him on the fire amid the flames and the red embers. One night Queen Metaneira caught her at it and uttered a scream of horror. Demeter removed the child from the fire and said: "It is a pity you interrupted me since I was in process of making your son immortal. Now he will have to suffer the law of all men."

She added sadly: "I shall therefore have done nothing that is not perishable."

And now you will say to me, for you would love to catch me out: "Why, Father Zeus, did you tell us that you were anxious at the sight of your cousin

Prometheus rubbing two sticks together, and why did you inflict on him the terrible punishment we know about, when you now tell us that fire already existed in the house of the King of Eleusis?" To which I make answer that you are a scatter-brained and conceited lot, always eager to interrupt another's discourse instead of waiting till he has made an end; with the result that, instead of showing off your brilliance as you imagine, you merely make evident your thoughtlessness and stupidity.

Whoever told you that fire did not exist before Prometheus? Where did you get hold of that idea?

On the contrary, there was fire in most men's houses. But it was fire lit by my lightning striking trees, or perhaps by a flow of red-hot lava spilt on my orders; it was *my* fire, loaned fire, of which men carried a part to their caves, their wattle and daub huts, or their first palaces built of superimposed stones. The fire had to be constantly watched and maintained; if, for one reason or another, I wished it to go out in such and such a house or district, I had merely to sow forgetfulness in the heads of the women who tended it, or make the waters of some river flood, or arrange for an abundant fall of rain. What do you suppose the heavy showers at the end of thunderstorms are for, except to extinguish, at the right moment, the fires that have slipped through my fingers? I controlled fire. Prometheus might make use of it; I did not prevent his utilizing the manifestation of fire. But what he was trying to do was to produce it himself.

He was not content with turning pointed twigs; he gathered flints and struck them against other stones; he stroked the backs of cats to feel their fur crackle with sparks; and he spent rather too much time wandering about volcanoes. He wanted to steal the principle of fire from me, and it was this which quite rightly displeased me.

You can now see that your interruption was uncalled for, and that a little good sense would have saved you from making it.

To return to my poor sister.

Having failed to make her host's child immortal, she wished at least to make him some exceptional present. For him she built with her own hands the first windmill where the breeze blows in the valley of Eleusis. The child was delighted and clapped his hands when he saw the white sails turning; he went to look at the wonderful toy every day; and, later, Demeter showed him how to harness the power of the sails to the millstone turning in the mortar.

An ancient bread, which my protégé, the learned Hippocrates of Cos, advised you to use, is called "triptos." The man who grinds the corn is called "tripteros." The name of the royal child to whom Demeter gave the windmill was Triptolemus.

But, for the moment, there was no grain to put under the millstone. For throughout the year Demeter stayed with the King of Eleusis, she neglected nature and it produced nothing. There were no crops and no harvest. The seed had not germinated in the dry and sterile soil. The Lady who must not be named, taking advantage of her mother's absence, everywhere spread anti-seed, the negative of the germ. Fields and gardens were deserts of desolation. I saw the human race in danger of dying of hunger; for even the cow, the gift of Uranus, could find no grass to eat, and its milk dried up.

It was in vain that I sent further messengers, and no mean ones, to my sister, beseeching her to abjure her disastrous obstinacy. They assumed all kinds of forms: an icy wind blowing under the door, a famished bird perching on the windowsill, a shivering child extending his hand to the passerby. They tried every means of touching her heart. But she would listen to none of them.

So I then summoned my brother Hades to a painful interview.

Interview with Hades.
Kore's Return.
The Pomegranate &
the Persea.

I talked to him for a long time; I described Demeter's condition to him and the state of nature since Kore's abduction.

"Your kingdom," I said to him in conclusion, "will have a sudden and surprising influx; but afterwards, and for all eternity, no new subjects will accrue to you. For once all life has become extinct for lack of food, death will consequently have no one left to send you. And so, instead of saving and continuing Uranus's work, we shall have merely destroyed it. Was this what we wanted when we took up arms against our father? Your marriage is a grave mistake for which we share the responsibility. I must ask you, however painful it is to me to go back on my word —and even more painful for you to make the sacrifice —but I must ask you, indeed beseech you, to give up Kore and send her back to the light of day."

I was greatly surprised by the calm with which Hades listened to me. I was prepared to offer him all kinds of compensations; I was ready to insist, argue and thunder if he refused them; I even envisaged, as a last resort, abdicating in his favor and giving him authority over the gods, if life on earth could be saved only at that price.

But I had no need to have recourse to these extremes. Hades replied that he accepted my reasons and would comply with my demand. Kore would be restored to her mother next morning.

So much goodwill was bound to cause me some perplexity. Where I had expected to confront an intractable husband, I had found nothing but understanding and courtesy. How could such detachment have replaced so ardent a passion? Had Hades already satiated his desires and become weary of Kore within the space of a year? Was he secretly disappointed in his marriage? Was she leading him what you might call an infernal life in the Infernal Regions? Yet, he in no way gave the impression that his marriage was an unhappy one.

A too easy surrender is always disquieting, and I wondered what trick lay behind it.

And another surprise was in store for me the next dawn, when Kore emerged from the abyss. She shielded her eyes with her hand as if to say: "What do they want with me? How vulgar and blinding the light of day is! Why have I been brought from my kingdom where I have a duty towards my adoring subjects? Oh, I know; here, too, they cannot get on without me!"

How changed she was! She had blossomed out in marriage. Her pallor had taken on the brilliance of mother of pearl; her shoulders seemed broader and she held her head higher. Her listless movements of the past had acquired a haughty air, and her old indolence had been transformed into a royal dignity. Everything went to show that she had found happiness in conformity with her character. She said some very pointed things about the vanity of life and the absurd activity on earth, which evinced great self-satisfaction. I had therefore not been wrong in giving her in marriage to the lord of the Infernal Regions. I had taken the right action but not, alas, at the right time!

Kore carefully counted the number of nymphs and supplicant mortals I had appointed to her train; concluding that she was being appropriately honored, she traveled slowly to Eleusis.

Demeter was wild with joy when she saw her daughter enter King Celeus's house; but at first Kore repulsed her. When, at last, she recognized the old woman in rags as her mother, she could not restrain her tears. All those present trembled and prostrated themselves at the sight of their divine embraces.

"My house is too small to receive such high and noble visitors," King Celeus said. "My house is unworthy of them."

"How can we prepare a feast to honor such guests as these?" said Queen Metaneira.

"Alas, indeed!" the servants chorused. "How can we prepare a feast and serve kykeon, when granary, larder and kitchen are bare?"

Even old Iobe was lamenting, muttering obscenities as was her habit.

But Kore put an end to their lamentations with a gesture.

"Do not worry about a meal," she said, "for I am not hungry."

These words seemed to make Demeter anxious.

"Kore, Kore, my dear daughter," she cried, "have you touched any food at all during your stay in the Infernal Regions?"

"I ate the fruit my husband gave me. And you must know that I am now no longer called Kore, but Persephone."

"Alas, alas!" Demeter cried. "Have you come back merely to give me such sad news? If Persephone is your new name, all is lost. Your marriage is indissoluble."

Once again her bosom was shaken with sobs; she scattered ashes on her hair, and went out, rending her rags, to return to sit on the Stone of Unhappiness.

When Persephone's adventures are related, you are always told of a pomegranate. In fact, the fruit Hades had plucked at the time of her abduction, and which indeed resembled a pomegranate except that it was more beautiful, more luscious and heavier, was called a "perseion"; and the tree which produced it, the "persea," was scarcely to be found except in Asia Minor and Egypt; it was a rare tree, and the places in which it grew were considered divine orchards.

You have opened a pomegranate; you have seen how the male seed is mingled with the pink female pulp, and that, when eating it, it is impossible to separate the one from the other. This is why the pomegranate is the fruit sacred to nuptials; the union it represents and sanctifies cannot be dissolved.

By eating a perseion in the kingdom of the dead, Kore had destroyed the two principles of the fruit, and at the same time bound herself forever to the ruler of those dark regions. And this was what her new name of Persephone expressed, for it means "murder of the persea."

*Another Assembly of
the Gods.
The Compromise.
Persephone's Annual
Journey & Demeter's
Transformations.*

I then summoned all the gods to Olympus. It was one of our first plenary assemblies. I asked our mother Rhea to be present, so as to confer greater solemnity on the meeting. Demeter made us all ashamed by appearing dressed in rags. She went to sit by our mother and looked like her ancestor.

"My dear girl," Rhea said to her, "is it not our common lot to be deprived of our children? Indeed, I myself . . ."

I requested the attention of the gods and explained the circumstances. Then I questioned Themis.

"What does the law say?" I asked.

"The law says that a wife must stay with her husband," Themis replied.

"Is that all the law says?" I asked.

"The law says that seed must germinate and the Earth flower."

I turned to Metis the Prudent.

"What does wisdom say, when law is opposed to law?"

Metis does not much care for speaking in public. She looked at Hades, then at Demeter, then at Themis, and then at me. At last she said: "When law is opposed to law, wisdom says that a compromise must be arrived at."

I then asked each side to explain his case. Hades's speech was a long argument, Demeter's a succession of sobs.

Meanwhile, Persephone was gazing calmly round the assembly, smiling at Hades, smiling at her mother, and seeming rather pleased to be the center of so important a debate.

In the end, I proposed the compromise I had thought out.

I know that one of your kings has since acquired a great reputation for suggesting that a child, claimed by two mothers, should be cut in half. Your Solomon would have cut a fine figure in history had the mothers agreed! In any case, no such procedure is applicable to immortals.

The solution I suggested seems to me to have been just as good. Persephone would divide her time between her husband and her mother; she would spend two-thirds of the year on Earth and the rest in the Infernal Regions.

"You are favoring life at the expense of death," my brother Hades said.

"The fact is that Demeter requires more than six months to do the work of the fields. There are slow-growing seeds and late harvests. Your harvest requires no effort on your part and the Fate Atropos is working for you at all seasons. Now, if you are prepared to shut the gates of your kingdom each year and spend a few months leisure up here with your wife, I know that a great many people will be wholly delighted."

But blind Hades is home-keeping; the idea of leaving his shadowy palace frightened him. And since he saw that all the gods approved my solution, he resigned himself to it. I am glad to record that, on this occasion, Prometheus gave me his whole-hearted support.

And so, each year, at the approach of spring, Persephone returns to Earth to be welcomed by her half-sisters the three Seasons and by all the nymphs of vegetation. Then Demeter, at sight of her daughter, recovers her former aspect. Once again her musical voice rings out in the valleys, and her bright smile shines through the spring showers. At her call, the tender buds open on the trees, the green shoots sprout from the furrows and soon the Earth is covered with leaves and flowers. Have you seen Demeter, at the hay-harvest, push back her hair bestrewn with sprigs of sweet-smelling hay from her brow on which pearls the sweat of happy labor? Have you seen the fields of ripe corn mysteriously quivering, rippling away to the horizon? It is Demeter passing by.

But as soon as the harvest has been got in and the last fruits of autumn have been picked, Persephone makes ready to depart. Hasten then, mortals, to plough your furrows, so that Demeter, with the last of her strength, may sow the seed which is to sleep in them for four months.

For as soon as Persephone has returned underground, Demeter becomes withered and bent; she turns into the old beggar-woman sitting on the Stone of Unhappiness. The wailing wind from her mouth drives the dead leaves along paths that are wet with her tears; the bare trees endlessly repeat the supplicating gesture of her emaciated arms; like her brow, the mountains are covered with snow and dark clouds; the ground is frozen, as insensible as the goddess's heart, and for all these months nature must share her mourning.

And so there it is, my dear sons; I could do no better.

And this is why you are accustomed to count four seasons, when I created only three; the last is the dead season, dedicated to the absent Persephone.

The Functions Attributed
to Triptolemus.
The Judges of
the Infernal Regions.
Adonis & Persephone.
The Institution of
the Mysteries.

When she left King Celeus's house to return
to take her place on Olympus, Demeter gave young
Triptolemus many more presents. She gave him a
grain of corn which she had been concealing in her
rags throughout the sterile year; at the same time she
taught her protégé the art of harnessing oxen and
how to make a ploughshare; and she appointed him to
spread the cultivation of wheat, the grinding of white
flour and the use of bread among the peoples.

Triptolemus lived to a great age, nearly as long as
the Atlantes. Then, when the hour of his death, which
she had been unable to spare him, arrived, Demeter
asked Persephone to give him a high position in her
realm of shadows. He is a judge in the Infernal Regions, a task he shares with my sons Aeacus, Rhada-
manthus and Minos, of whom the first was to be born
of the nymph Aegina, and the other two of Europa.

With them, he sorts out the new arrivals and weighs souls. To the just and the initiated, he awards peace and the mysterious felicity of participation in the divine essence; the others are condemned to drawing water in darkness with a sieve.

Hades and Persephone, unlikely as it may seem, have continued to be a happy couple. Since they are separated for eight months and have but four for love, their yearly meetings are like new nuptials. Many human marriages might follow their example with advantage.

Though free in her behavior during her annual journey to Earth, Persephone has remained a faithful wife. I mean more faithful than most wives. Conscious of her dignity as a queen, and not by nature quick to be carried away, she was able to discourage advances. She had, rather late, one adulterous passion; it was for the handsome Adonis, whose blood, when he was wounded, tinted the rose and the anemone. She vied with Aphrodite in desire for him. And since nothing happens to anyone, whether god or mortal, but that which is in character, and because each one of us, mortal or god, is impelled by his nature towards similar situations, here again the conflict had to be resolved by a compromise. Every winter, Adonis accompanies Persephone to the Infernal Regions. Hades has got used to his presence, and of the tenebrous trio they form, it is not Adonis who has the most satisfaction.

You must also know that the persea disappeared from among the species.

In memory of the many important events that had taken place under his roof, and so that Demeter and

Persephone might henceforth meet in a building
worthy of them, King Celeus built a temple at Eleusis
and it has been embellished through the centuries. For
a long while great celebrations, started by Triptolemus,
were held there, and they rejoiced the gods.

For three days at the end of October, Persephone's
departure was accompanied by ceremonies to which
only married women were admitted. In February the
virgins celebrated the return of Kore, bringing the
dispersed energies back to the Earth and restoring to
Demeter her fecundating joy.

And also, every five years, those among you, mortals,
who were worthy, having purified yourselves in the
sea, came in long processions, from Athens and all the
cities of Greece, to be initiated into the eternal chain
of life and death.

The Eleusinian mysteries are not, as you are too inclined to believe, a matter of whispered instruction,
and the initiation is not an admission into a closed so-
ciety with secret understandings among its members.

The mysteries are performances, spectacles that lead
the spirit to a state of light and knowledge, which is
incommunicable between man and man by means of
ordinary language, because it is the hearing and the
understanding of the language of the gods. The initiation consists in performing certain actions which are
a preparation for the understanding of the spectacles.

What shall I have revealed to you, when I tell you
the following?

"The neophyte, having been purified, first drinks the
kykeon. Then he puts his hands in the basket. He

fumbles and places something in the hamper. He then takes something from the hamper and replaces it in the basket. He has touched grain, soil and wool in the basket; and, in the hamper, the male and female organs of generation."

Nothing more can be said, nor has need to be. The most perfect object of contemplation is an ear of corn plucked in silence.

You merely need to know that the mysteries prepare a man to die well. He who has contemplated them, when he goes down below the Earth, knows the end of life but also its beginning; and his dearest hopes are assured to him till the end of time.

Eleusis, Eleusis! Today I see other columns but those of temples rising in your sky. I see, mortals my sons, the rows of your factory chimneys, and smokes other than those of sacrifices coming from them. I see some among you patiently searching that sacred soil and turning over its ancient stones to recover the secrets you have allowed to be lost.

Question Hecate; she still stands at the crossroads of your quest; she also lingers about ruins and tombs. Perhaps, with her two torches, she will light the road you are seeking between your past and your future.

THE SIXTH EPOCH

*The Desert
or the Chain*

The Lady Who Must
Not Be Named.
Depression.
Oceanus's Advice.

When Persephone's drama, which had caused me trouble and anxiety for over a year, was at last resolved, do you imagine that I felt freed, relieved and happy? On the contrary, I was seized, as if by some pernicious disease, with a dark, disastrous passion for Demeter's other daughter, the blind and sterile Lady who must not be named.

Surely the Destinies presiding over Demeter the fecund were compensating: Hades had fallen passionately in love with the child she had had by me, and now I was haunted by the child she had had by Poseidon the unsatisfied.

But can one call attraction what is in fact a bitter detachment from everything, passion what is an incapacity to feel any desire whatever, and love what is disaffection and a total inability to love?

Obsession better describes my grievous and desolate state while I was under the sway of the sad Mistress.

You may have thought, perhaps, that this nameless goddess was death. Not at all; death has its name and

its god, Thanatos, the brother of Sleep; it has its at-
tendant Fate and its kingdom ruled over by Hades. It
works silently in your shadow and, till the ultimate
hour, does not prevent your enjoying life. If yours is
a superficial nature, you can forget this patient fiancée;
if you belong to the race of the wise, you can prepare
yourself by meditation or initiation for a serene ac-
ceptance of her inevitable embrace; you can brave her
and tempt her and feel stronger and happier for having
escaped her arms; and the very fear with which she
inspires you incites you to create and derive the more
profit from moments of illumination.

The Lady is quite other. She is the principle of nega-
tion; she is death in life and life in death.

You have seen that most of the gods fulfill two functions, one in the cosmic or natural order, the other in
relation to you for that which is a reflection of the
divine cosmos in your nature and being. You will also
have realized that these two functions are not distinct
in their essence but derive from the same principle.

But the Lady withers the flower and rots the fruit
on the tree.

Similarly she withers thought and rots joy, desire
and will power on the tree of the soul.

She it is who conceals in a sort of mist the paths that
link you to your fellows and the world; she it is who
destroys in you the will to undertake, act and com-
municate, who takes away your appetite for life while
in no way diminishing your agony at the thought of
death. She traces a circle about you which seems to you
impassable; she turns against you, to deny and destroy

you, the powers you brought into the world construct it and prove yourself in it. In this invisible prison of which she is both the bars and the jailer, your mind can do nothing but turn in on itself and contemplate its own unhappiness.

The Lady presides over that desert of the soul you know so well though you cannot precisely define it; for want of a better term you call it "melancholy," or "accidie."

A sad, disheartened, despairing Zeus, with no enthusiasm to create or joy in ruling is almost inconceivable. And yet it was so.

I no longer accompanied Demeter through the burgeoning countryside. I no longer spoke the grateful word which Hestia's labors in the home deserved. The gayety of the Nereids as they chased each other laughing across the sea seemed to me absurd and irritating. I was no longer proud of my daughters the Seasons and the Muses. I no longer talked to Memory, for even to remember was painful to me. The anti-mistress placed a distance between me and all the other goddesses; and many of them were distressed by my incomprehensible aloofness.

The gloomy gravity with which I announced my decisions, and which passed for a sign of concentrated thought, was merely an ill-fitting mask to conceal my solitude.

But melancholy always has its origin in a dissatisfaction with ourselves for which we must discover the reason; it is self-reproach which opens the door to it.

Till the abduction of Persephone, the battles I had had to fight had been solely against forces exterior to myself. For the first time I was faced with the consequences of my own actions. For Persephone was my creation; her marriage had taken place by my decision. I could, of course, accuse Demeter of a too possessive mother love, and Hades of folly and slyness; but I could not deny my preponderant responsibility. I thus realized that every action we thought happy and proper when we performed it contains nevertheless the seed of suffering or of some disastrous consequence.

The chain of joy and sorrow is an endless one, as solid and regular as that of life and death. I reached a point where I regretted being the king of the gods; that is to say, the chain's eternal driving-force. "What folly," I thought, "impelled me to wish to rule?"

I was never so unhappy as at this time when, triumphant, feared, obeyed, envied and loved, the universe seemed to be in a conspiracy to present me with every circumstance for happiness. I often thought nostalgically of the days of fear, danger and hope, when I was planning my war and had not yet won it.

Some nights, blank of both love and sleep, I went silently to the shores of Crete, without allowing either my mother or Amaltheia to see me; I gazed lingeringly at my native island and at the hills on which I had run, played and waited, still in my pristine form, when I was a man and not yet a god. I also contemplated by the light of the moon my effigy sculpted at the summit of the mountain. I wondered about this heavy profile, ineluctably awaiting me from the beginning of time, which I was now beginning to resemble. I was tempted to lie down beneath the rock and sleep there forever, leaving the government of the world to whoever wished to assume it. Anyone could make the sad chain turn as well as I; and if he did it less well, what did it matter?

One night, I saw a disturbance on the face of the sea. The waters opened; my uncle Oceanus appeared, shaking his white head, his beard curling with foam. He came to sit beside me on the shore.

"Nephew Zeus," he said. "I have seen you looking unhappy for many long days. What is the cause of your suffering?"

"Is my misery so obvious?" I asked.

"It can be guessed by anyone who has lived longer than you have."

"I think I made a mistake in fathering Persephone," I said.

"The mistake, if it was a mistake," Oceanus replied, "is now repaired. You should therefore no longer be concerned about it. Persephone is merely an apparent cause to which your mind clings in order to conceal from itself a deeper reason."

"Perhaps I am suffering from having loved several goddesses, none of whom could retain my affections."

I said this rather contritely, for among those I had abandoned were two of Oceanus's daughters. But Oceanus is very broad-minded; he sees things clearly and he sees them whole; and no doubt, as he contemplated the universe, my fate seemed to him more important than that of his own daughters. He replied:

201

"You may well have many more mistresses, and indeed you will have them. And you may also, if you so wish, go back to those you have abandoned. Your loneliness does not depend on your women."

"The fault therefore lies with Her who must not be named."

"No," Oceanus said. "The black Lady is an effect, not a cause. You could have prevented her being born. And you could also have prevented her approaching you, for she is blind. It was you who surrendered yourself to her; she is a punishment you have inflicted on yourself."

"In that case, my profoundly thinking uncle, what is the real cause? Tell me, if it can help me!"

Oceanus nodded his wrinkled brow and blew on the surface of the waters. Then he said: "You are suffering because you no longer have a father, and you are punishing yourself for having shut him up in Tartarus."

"No, really!" I cried. "How could I regret a father who wanted to devour me and whom I knew only as my enemy in a war? What possible pang could his disappearance cause me?"

"Not so loud, do not shout," Oceanus said. "The world has no need to be informed of these things. Of course, your father hated you, and you hated him. But neither love nor hate can alter the facts. You have no one in authority over you now. A loving father is a protection. A father who hates you is an obstacle; but an obstacle is still a support. While your father ruled, he seemed to you to be responsible for everything; but now it is you who are answerable to others and for others, but above all to yourself and for yourself; and you cannot unload your burden onto anyone else. Young though you are, you have become old Zeus, for one becomes old the moment one ceases to be a son. You are hemmed in with requests which you either satisfy or disappoint; you are invoked; but whom can you invoke? I remembered what happened when Uranus disappeared, both to me who loved him, and to my brothers who hated him. We were all equally affected, and if Cronus destroyed the better part of the inheritance he had coveted, it was to punish himself. You have not destroyed the inheritance, but you feel its weight."

"Uncle, uncle," I said, "you are wiser and more learned than I. Why did you not take over the government of the world instead of encouraging me to do so?"

"Precisely because I am wise. Because you had both the desire and the aptitude for it. Because I would have suffered an even greater desolation than yours at being both the first and the oldest. Because, when you became king, it was necessary that there should still be an elder to understand you and talk to you at bitter moments such as this."

Dawn was pale in the sky. I knew I had to return to Olympus and appear on the threshold at the hour when the gods on duty set off to work.

"Uncle," I asked, "is there any remedy for the ailment you have diagnosed in me?"

"Have sons," Oceanus replied. "Take a wife, or several, and have sons. No longer just daughters; males now. To recognize oneself in young and rising strength, to watch young gods growing up, to have to beware they do not supplant you, to do your best to keep their admiration, and to be continually mindful to retain their love—which is the most subtle form of struggle to preserve one's power—this is now the only way by which you can break the spell of black loneliness. And you will recover your taste for pleasure."

Thereupon, Oceanus plunged back into the deep, while I returned to my throne about which the clouds were beginning to turn rosy.

Mortals, you have depicted me as a god who was often thoughtful and often gay, nor have you been wrong. But no one has ever told you that I was a happy god.

After the Melancholia.
The Night with Aphrodite.
Frenzy & Loneliness.

Melancholy is to the soul what winter is to the fields. It withers, buries and kills, but only to allow new seed to germinate. It is at once tillage and gestation.

When I had sufficiently thought over Oceanus's words and had succeeded in turning my eyes away from the contemplation of myself, I saw two tall goddesses sitting not far from my throne, one on the edge of the sky and the other on a summit of the Earth. The first was my aunt Aphrodite; she was casually playing with the belt of light about her waist. The second was my sister Hera, who was fondling a peacock. They were pretending to be absorbed in their own thoughts, but they were both secretly watching me and each other.

When Aphrodite saw me looking at her, she smiled, and when I smiled back she got up to go away. Her dress, made out of a transparent blue cloud, concealed none of her perfect proportions. Her belt of light, hemmed with sun, outlined the curve of her hips; it was impossible to watch the fringe of the goddess's belt trembling against her stomach and not feel a quivering of desire. Aphrodite was indeed the last star of night present in the morning sky. Her smile seemed to imply: "You can find in my arms at dawn the realization of the most exquisite dreams the mind can conceive during the night. You have only to dare."

I was already rising to follow her when, above the spreading peacock's tail, I saw the beautiful brow and the dark, moving, watching eyes of my sister Hera. I postponed joining Aphrodite; but all that day I put greater energy into my tasks; I remanded a renewal of activity from the world; and the gods whispered to each other: "Zeus appears to be happy again."

The peace and cool of evening were already spreading over the Earth, though the light was still clear, when Aphrodite reappeared on the other side of the sky. She was now wearing a rose dress, even more transparent than that of the morning, and she had sewn bright spangles to her belt. I cannot assert that Aphrodite always dresses in the best of taste; I simply mean that the diversity, audacity and richness of the ornaments she wears make it certain that she never passes unremarked. But her greatest riches, and also her greatest audacity, appear when she divests herself of her apparel. And this she half did, when she had sat down on her vesperal bed. Her breasts bare in the sky, she smiled at me. As yet there were no stars round her. We began to talk to each other with our eyes again.

"Am I not," her eyes said to me, "the hope you have been pursuing all day? Am I not the destined reward for the labors you have accomplished?"

"Then come to me," my eyelids replied, "and charm my night."

"No, not with that tiresome Hera so obstinately lingering near your throne and watching us from behind her peacock fan. But come to join me on my couch. We will wrap ourselves in the sheets of shadow; and I will give you both frenzy and repose. . . ."

Repose? It was a promise that was not honored in the event. Never, in all my amorous career, have I spent so trying a night. And, believe me, it was not by love that Aphrodite exhausted me. She never stopped talking about herself till dawn. She was still talking when the sun began to shine.

But what else could one expect? She had, so she said, slept the whole day so as to be beautiful and fresh, so as to display all her charms to delight, distract and conquer me. And she would sleep all the next day too. It was as if repose for her was the object of anxiety and effort, and that she set about it as other people set to work. It was the same with her appearance. What care and labor she put into perfecting it! And for whom was this exhausting process undertaken? For me; and so that she might be worthy of attracting my eye.

Tonight her hair might be brown; but tomorrow she would be red-headed or blonde. She knew how to change her coloring. She would go and dip her hair in the sea; she would wash it in the juice of various secret plants; she would spread it out on a cloud and remain still for hours in the heat of the sun. I wanted to see her blonde, did I not? I had not suggested it; but she had made up her mind. By the next day she would have accomplished the great feat of becoming a blonde Aphrodite. Indeed, would the king of the gods ever find a more docile slave?

At one moment, she seemed to be interested in my work.

"What have you done today," she asked, "that will make me proud of you?"

She spoke as if I already belonged to her. Nor did she listen to my reply. She knew very well what I needed to be happy. Love is never deceived, and she was nothing but loving! I needed a goddess at my side whose splendor would increase my power over my subjects. My lightning inspired them with fear; her smile would win me their devotion. Were we not made for each other, I the most powerful of gods, and she the most beautiful of goddesses? She had determined to belong to no one but me.

It seemed to me that the moment had come to grant so charming a wish, and, pressing myself against her side, I showed her that she had no need of further effort to bring me to the point she desired. From her lowered lashes, and her ecstatic smile, on which the moon was now shining, I thought she was ready to abandon herself. I was starting to undo her belt, when she suddenly began talking about her father.

I have told you how Aphrodite was born from the waves, and in what circumstances. This partly explains the high sense she has of her own importance; conscious of being the progeny of the sky, she has always looked on the world as if it were made to revolve about her. But was this the moment to recall these things? Nor was it a matter of evoking our tragic births, our orphan lot, and thereby arousing a mutual tenderness, a sense of closeness to each other. No, indeed; it was a matter of inheritance.

Tethys had at her disposal the infinite treasure of her husband Oceanus, and her palace was overflowing with primordial riches; Amphitrite shared the kingdom of the sea with Poseidon; Memory had her recollections and the valley of the two springs; Demeter had nature, flowers and rich harvests. All the goddesses had been provided for; Aphrodite alone, according to her, had received nothing in this general distribution.

"Is it nothing," I replied, "to have supreme beauty and the eternal power of inspiring desire? All the immortals, and the mortals too, are envious and jealous of you."

"Envy is a menace and not a fortune," Aphrodite said. "Beauty requires some tribute which proves its supremacy."

She had discovered or been told that the palace of her father Uranus, now destroyed, had been built of colored and transparent stones, which reflected the light with wonderful brilliance. She had heard that some of these stones, which had been the work of the One-Eyed and the Hundred-Handed, still existed, buried in the entrails of the mountains. Was it true that emeralds, sapphires and rubies gave out the rays of original forces, and that each gem contained a peculiar and beneficent energy? Oh, how had Uranus been able to solidify, in amethyst and crysolite, in lapis and opal, each variation of the components of light, and, in the diamond, crystalize light itself? Was not each heavenly body represented on Earth by one of these stones?

"They are a small part of father's work," Aphrodite said in a voice so moving that it would have drawn tears from your eyes.

Well, there it was; she was asking for nothing but these colored stones as a keepsake. They would protect her against the menace of envy. Was it not a very modest request and could I be so hard as to refuse it? Aphrodite intended to sew the stones onto the belt whose fastening I was beginning to find rather complicated; my fingers were becoming exasperated with it.

Mortals my sons, forgive me the promise I then made. It has cost you dear.

But ardent as I was, and naïve as you still are, I thought that Aphrodite, now that she was satisfied, would have no other desire in mind but love. For a moment, she gave me that illusion, for she undid her belt herself with superb facility and evident pleasure.

"And it was thus," she said, letting her dress fall from her, "that I emerged from the sea. I am the Anadyomene."

She did not even give me time to express my wonder. It was so natural to her to be admired! She already had another request in mind, this time about the sea, which had been her cradle. She wanted me to make her a present of something which would remind her of the sea. Oh, just some little thing, some trifle: the oyster!

I had already given her the diamond; I might just as well give her this placid mollusk.

Oh, my poor children, how many of you have burst your hearts by fishing for those damned oysters of hers, and to acquire their accidental contents!

"It is because pearls are like my teeth," Aphrodite murmured, leaning tenderly on my shoulder, "and mother of pearl is like my nails. And now the other goddesses will never be able to rival me."

And off the inexhaustible chatterbox went again. The other goddesses, if she were to be believed, and particularly those whom I had loved, were all disfigured by some imperfection. Demeter really took too little trouble about herself. Had I noticed Demeter's hands? Was it true that Eurynome was sadly afflicted with the lips of a fish? And how had Themis, who though intelligent, of course, was so massive and so cold, managed to inspire me with desire?

"I do not know exactly how she inspired it, but I know very well that she satisfied it."

Oh, what had I said? Aphrodite began to press me with questions as to how each of my conquests made love. But she answered her questions herself. Moreover, could one call them conquests? It was I, idiot that I was, encumbered with my power, who had each time allowed myself to be conquered. None of these goddesses was really worthy of me. And Aphrodite asserted, with a fierce certitude, that I could never have attained to the supreme transports in their arms. Jealous, she? Of whom? Could one be jealous of such evident inferiors?

Yes, my sons, I know! I ought to have seized some handy cloud to gag her with, or got up and left her to rave to herself. But two-thirds of the way through the night, the will becomes feeble, while desire is still vigorous. One always thinks that one will make up the next moment for all the lost hours. And Aphrodite's eyes were continually promising it. Besides, she was so beautiful to look at, one leg stretched out, the other bent, with her perfect knee making an angle against the field of stars. She was naked and consenting, and all was understood between us. And if what she said was irritating, her voice was marvelous. It was merely

a matter of waiting for the moment of perfect harmony. Confidingly, the goddess sought my hand, min-
gling her fragile fingers with mine. Dared one be rough
and risk destroying the accord that was now so near?

It will not surprise you to learn that the grievous
Priapus is one of Aphrodite's sons. But I am not his
father.

For having touched my lips with the lightest of
kisses, the mere promise of a kiss, she immediately
cried: "From now on I want to be the only one. Swear
to me that I shall be the only one!"

It was an embarrassing demand! But once again it
was Aphrodite who replied to it. She had no need of
an oath. She *knew* that from now on I could belong
to no one but her; my derisory memories would be
effaced, and no new goddess would ever be able to
tempt me.

"I shall be the only one, because I shall be all of
them! I shall be the Aphrodite Pandemos of vulgar and
banal love. We shall lie together simply in the fields
like the rustic goatherd and shepherdess, or like the
sailor on coming into port with the first servant girl
he meets."

"Very well, so be it," I said, "let us begin like that."

She restrained me with a pressure of her fingers.

"I shall accompany you in all your battles; I shall be
the Aphrodite Nicephore, bringer of victories."

"What weapons," I asked in surprise, "will you carry
to support me?"

"My love, and your continuing ardor in conquering

me. . . . And for you I shall also become a mother; I shall let my beautiful body grow heavy and suffer the pains of childbirth. I shall be called Venus Genetrix; virgins, widows and barren wives will be my suppliants so that I may grant them that burdensome felicity."

At this point, I began to think, and felt a certain anxiety about the children I might have by so inspired a goddess.

"I shall never let you grow weary," she went on, "for I shall be both lubricity and impiety, the Hetaira and the Anosia. I shall offer myself to you in the shape of animals; I shall turn myself into a heifer, a she-ass or a sheep. Or again, assuming the form of a woman, I shall make you take on, for our more brutal couplings, the nature of a he-goat, a bull or a wild ass."

In what strange guise the last researches of Uranus the grafter were reappearing!

"Then, returning to our greatest splendor, we shall unite in view of all the other gods, obliging them to copulate all around us as if they were reflections of ourselves multiplied to infinity by a hundred mirrors. The ingenuity of our games will astonish even ourselves."

The night was coming to an end; dawn was breaking in the East; and Aphrodite continued to describe herself, invent a role for herself, and dream of the future.

"I shall be the Aphrodite Porne, whom you will treat without consideration, who will give you her body like a piece of merchandise, and from whom you will be able to demand the most degrading caresses."

"There are others," I thought, "who would give them me for a lesser price."

"Nevertheless, I shall always remain the Uranian Aphrodite, the goddess of sublime, pure, disincarnate and celestial love. . . ."

Upon which I decided that, for one night, I had had quite enough of that particular love. I got up, at once exhausted and unsatisfied, all desire destroyed. But to leave her was another matter. I had yet to know the agonized, tearful and misunderstood Aphrodite, the Aphrodite who was spendthrift of the dawn.

"Stay," she said, clasping my knees. "The world can wait. I will give you more than the whole universe. Oh, I was on the point of being so happy!"

At last, as I was determined to go, she became an outraged Aphrodite and cried: "And so throughout a whole night the king of the gods has not even ravished me!"

As I descended the staircase of the clouds, I said to her over my shoulder: "Two people cannot live together when they both want to be the first."

This was how we parted, each of us as dissatisfied with the other as with himself.

Since then, Aphrodite has often asserted that it all depended on her and that, had she wished . . . I can claim as much. At the assembly of the gods, our relations are courteous, but distant and full of mistrust.

People have often been astonished that Aphrodite has never been numbered among my passions. Some people, indeed, have never been able to understand why I did not choose her for wife and invite her to share my throne. To look at us, they said, we seemed so admirably suited to each other!

Well, ask the admirable, hard-working Hephaestus, my eldest son, who allowed himself to be seduced by her, the unfortunate fellow, and married her; ask Aphrodite's innumerable lovers to whom she is suited!

Oh, no, believe me, mortals: rather an ugly woman and I have had a few; no long amorous career can be pursued for a lesser price—rather a fool, a blunderer, a whiner, a shrew, an over-possessive woman; rather anyone, indeed, than that beauty in love only with herself!

When she assumes human shape, admire her hair, her bosom and her ankles, the charm of her gestures, the melodious quality of her voice; watch her on that stage where she performs such prodigies, appearing each day in a different role and yet being always herself.

But, if you are like me, maintain the chasm of illusion between yourself and her. For when she makes a stage of life, she becomes Helen, Phaedra or Pasiphae.

She considers herself worthy to be loved only by kings, but she wants them to avow themselves her slaves; yet when they behave as slaves, how can they be deserving of her love? Is that not so, Menelaus? Is that not so, Theseus? Is that not so, Mark Antony? Is that not so, Justinian?

In her disappointment, she offers herself to captain, poet, orator and scribe, to gladiator, falconer and drover, persuading each of them that in her arms he will be a king. She even offers herself to the bull; is that not so, Minos? For nothing male must escape her.

Unhappy Aphrodite, condemned to embrace forever nothing but her solitude, since, in the throes of her desire, she demands of the lover in her arms that he should admit that he is nothing!

For two brief moments, at the rise and decline of day, Venus can imagine that she is the sole luminary in the sky, and try to persuade us of it. But her lonely shining, for which she demands our adoration, is of no use to us, for the light of day is already, or still remains, over the world.

When I returned to Olympus that morning, I was grey of face and tired of eye. My sister Hera, who saw me come home, refused to believe the truth.

Hera's Day.
The Destiny of Greece.
Plans for Olympus.

If I have scarcely mentioned my sister Hera, whom you also call Juno, it is because till now there has been little to say about her.

You know that, regurgitated from Cronus's entrails, she had been given asylum by our grandmother Gæa, and was then confided to Oceanus and Tethys who had brought her up.

Since then, she had done nothing, or at least nothing of note. She had never spoken at the assembly of the gods; she was content to listen attentively to others. She had asked for nothing in the sharing out of the world, nor shown a taste for any particular work; she never even suggested she should help anyone else in their labors, and left Hestia to tend the hearth, and Demeter to work in the garden. Nevertheless, she gave no impression of laziness and always rose early.

Hera has heavy, thick, abundant and very wavy black hair, which she tends and dresses with care; the gesture with which she loosens it, shakes her head and lets it fall to her waist is a beautiful one. I had sometimes surprised this gesture at evening and it had moved me. But had not Hera arranged things so that I should surprise her?

Beneath the equal arcs of her eyebrows, Hera has huge almond-shaped eyes whose clear color is somewhere between grey and green; you admire them as they gaze at you.

Her tunic, which is always carefully pleated, reveals the whole of her arms which are splendid, and conceals beneath an harmonious drapery her hips which are rather wide and heavy.

So that morning on which I returned somewhat ingloriously from Aphrodite, I found Hera on the threshold of Olympus. Was she awaiting me? She gave no sign of it and seemed to be absorbed in contemplating the world.

I wanted company and distraction.

"Come," I said, "let us go down and take a walk among men."

Hera walked in step with me, which is so important. She was not one of those goddesses who trot along, loiter, stop, oblige you to slow your pace because they are breathless, or weigh on your arm like a reproach. Hera and I walked with the same stride, and we were able to look at the surrounding countryside and to talk.

Greece was not then precisely as she is now; certain upheavals, particularly those due to the misdeeds of the giants, were to alter the contours here and there. And man also was not such as he was to become as a result of disaster, effort, and the numerous gifts I and my children have since made him.

The destiny of Greece was only at its inception. But Greece already afforded that mixture of the gentle and the picturesque, that contrast between tragic mountain and quiet plain, that juxtaposition of barren spur and verdant valley, that infinitely indented coastline, that pervasive inter-penetration of land and water, of aggressive rock and fluid sea, that perpetual variation of light, those horizons which consist not of one precise boundary between the visible and the invisible but of a succession of horizons that become increasingly veiled like the farther reaches of the consciousness, all that indeed which made of this country a place where man might recognize, develop and exalt himself.

Greece is a small country; but so is your hand small; and yet everything is marked in it, the valleys of your future, the hills of your aptitudes, the confluences of your loves, the crosses of your dangers; it is your palm which concentrates and applies all your energies; and it is those minute fingers of yours that feel, grasp, examine, design, model and construct all your works.

Seen from the height from which the gods see it, Greece resembles a hand. She is the hand of humanity, the active palm in which everything has been shaped, or reshaped, between the diffused memories of one lost Golden Age and the ideal of another Golden Age still to be built.

Greece is on the scale of men, or, more precisely, she is the *scale* of man. Her natural dangers are not greater than man can surmount, nor the tragedy of the elements worse than she can bear and remain conscious. The mountains are high, precipitous and difficult to climb, but they can be crossed. The barren plateau is never so wide as not to afford the traveler a spring and shade before exhaustion overtakes him. The familiar, tideless sea bounds the pine-grove or prolongs the field, and invites you to embark for the next bay, promontory or visible island lying in its golden haze, stages on the road to adventure.

In other wetter or more sun-crushed climates, man seems to dissolve in time and space, to become diluted in a thick vegetable mass, or to crumble away like sand. Elsewhere, in too vast spaces or in inclement latitudes, man can subsist, work and conquer only by assembling in his hundreds or millions to vanquish distance, organize himself against extremes of climate, and triumph over the vastness of nature. He is no longer man; he becomes *men*, a swarming mass of innumerable tracks and overlapping actions.

In Greece, human action remains particular, ever charged with its peculiar significance. Each vine-grower who treads the black grapes in the sticky vat is *the* vine-grower; each spinner who turns her spindle beside the road is *the* spinner; the sobbing child is *the* orphan; and the passing soldier with his spear on his shoulder is *the* soldier.

It is this character of particularity assumed by each human action which designated Greece to be the land of myths; that is to say, to furnish the definitions which stand forever as the pattern of man's relations both with his own kind and with all the visible or secret forces of the universe. And this is the destiny of Greece.

These things had never been so clear to me as on that day in early spring when I walked with my sister Hera. Doubtless, to see and appreciate vividly you need a companion, provided she also knows how to look and understand, and that her thought and her step are in tune with yours. Then the fleeting impression, by being expressed, acquires weight and duration; then between sight and remark, between remark and reply, a silken cloth is woven, of which one of you holds the warp and the other the woof, and on it the colors of the world take form.

I was surprised by Hera's knowledge and of the good use she made of it. She seemed to be informed about everything. I asked her how she had acquired so much information, and I discovered that she had

set herself methodically to learn from the beginning
of my reign. She had received instruction from Memory and Themis; she appeared to have won the confidence and friendship of my first mistresses, even of
Metis the Prudent; she spoke of these goddesses with
propriety and reverence. But why had she made this
great effort to learn about everything when she apparently did nothing with her knowledge?

"To prepare myself," she said with a sort of detachment.

And I wondered: "Prepare herself for what?" Really,
I am overmodest at times!

Hera had also made friends with my daughters the
Muses, the Seasons and the Fates, and assured me she
was fond of them. She was a little reticent only about
strong Athena.

She was aware of everything I had done since my
election; she understood the reasons for my actions,
and marveled at the number of works on which I was
engaged at the same time.

"Just recently," I said, "my ardor has considerably
diminished."

Well, it had not seemed so to her. I was therefore
even cleverer than she had believed, since I was able
to conceal my failings. . . .

She remembered seeing me handling the lightning
during the battle against the Titans; she said that she
admired me, and I am sure she was being sincere.
Would she otherwise have taken such pains to please
me?

I soon came to look on her as the most intelligent

221

and accomplished of the goddesses of the new generation. And she was robust, too! She kept up her splendid, gallant stride.

Indeed, it was a happy day! I felt reconciled both
to myself and the universe. From the insect to the sun,
everything was pleasant, engaging and delightful, and
took its place in an harmonious sympathy.

And what a pleasure it is to conceive great projects
when they are attentively listened to, and the pertinent,
eager question encourages you.

Had I chosen Olympus as my permanent residence?

"Till now, I have been hesitating," I told Hera. "But
seeing Greece as she appears to me today, I really think
her highest mountain must remain my home."

Hera agreed. Olympus had been favorable to me so
far. She herself liked Olympus. The large amphitheater
amid the peaks lent itself perfectly to the assemblies
of the gods.

"And if as you tell me," she went on, "your greatest
plans concern man, there is no better place from which
to watch over Uranus's incompleted masterpiece and
pursue its perfecting."

But she thought that Olympus should be more sump-
tuously organized, and considered that I should be
surrounded by a more numerous, attentive and hier-
archical court. She seemed to have a gift for organization.

It is thus, my sons, that some women make themselves indispensable by complicating your lives. They
organize so great a household for you that you can
no longer do without them to run it.

"We might sometimes give feasts to the gods, which would not only be a manifestation of your supreme power but also serve as models for the feasts of men."

In the euphoria created by our walk, I did not notice this first "we" which was uttered so naturally. Hera and I were approaching the coast. We saw a beach on which a fisherman was grilling the fish he had caught over embers.

The Four Pillars of Life.
The Happy Fisherman.

A fire lit by the seashore makes a conjunction of the four elements. And there is no sight, I can assure you, more pleasing to the gods.

I have told you that nothing can be created except by the aggressive attraction of two concrete forces combining and annihilating themselves in a third and new reality. And thus you have thought that Number is a triad.

But I must now reveal to you that four forces are necessary, and that their complementary antagonisms must be ceaselessly destroying and recomposing, to assure the perpetuation of life.

For the third element of the triad would be only an

absence of attraction, an abstraction, congealed in a terminal solitude, if it were not in its turn the aggressor and the aggressed, the lover, devourer and devoured, at a force other than itself.

If, therefore, three is the Number of all creation, four is that of the invisible pillars of all life.

Do not forget this when, your eyes glued to various lenses, you set about exploring things that are, in relation to your situation, infinitely small or infinitely large, and even to piercing the secret of your own genes.

And do not forget, either, that each element of the three, as of the four, is triple, according to whether it appears in its principle, its manifestation or its non-presence. Thus the three are nine and the four are twelve. . . .

I know some among you who will not take their heads in their hands at this, but immediately feel justified in their need for more women than their own wife. There is equally no bar to their understanding the urge that on occasion impels their wives to consume themselves in another ardor in the arms of a lover. . . .

These are the things, among many others, which appear to the gods in the flame of a single fire of vine twigs burning by the seashore.

The understanding between Hera and myself that day was so perfect that we had merely to exchange a glance. We both reduced ourselves to human shape and, holding each other by the hand, went up to the fisherman and his fire.

The fisherman invited us to sit down and share his

fish. He gave with the noble and simple gesture which is to be found only among those who have nothing or have everything, the true poor or the true kings.

This fisherman had, like a sovereign, fabulous treasures at his disposal, nor were they limited by the derisory bounds of even moderate wealth. He had the sand on which he invited us to sit, the inexhaustible sea in which his able hands had caught the fish, the embers he had carried from some nearby hearth, and the breeze which livened the fire. In that precise place and for that fleeting moment, he was the absolute king of the four elements.

He asked no questions and treated us with the greatest possible politeness. For the Greek, every traveler may be a god disguised. Nor is the Greek wrong; it is you, you scoffers, who are in error.

Never, in all the travels I have made disguised as a human, have I tasted such exquisitely palatable food as those fish fresh from the sea, cooked in their own oil, salted with their own salt, and scented with the aroma of the twigs over which they had been grilled. We ate hungrily, burning our fingers and lips a little.

When we had finished, the fisherman thanked us.

"Why do you thank us, fisherman," I asked him, "when it is we who owe you gratitude?"

"Because I have had the opportunity of seeing two young, handsome, happy people in love with each other; and because, thanks to you, I shall never feel poor again, since I, lonely and impoverished as I am, have been able to give to those who have everything."

Hera and I looked at each other; our hands sought

each other's and our fingers, still black with burnt scales, interlaced of their own accord.

What did I tell you a moment ago about the Number four? There was Hera with her beautiful arms; there was I, Zeus; and there was love. But there had to be the fisherman, too, the fourth element, so that love should become reality to us and the forces of life should begin to work.

Happy couples who travel in Greece, bear it constantly in mind that we gods do not always assume a shape. We often slip into you without your knowing it so that the right deed may be accomplished at the right time. Then, on some beach similar to a hundred others, or when passing through some white village, or at a frugal table set beside a dusty road, or simply at sight of a cypress with its slender top cutting across the vault of the sky, you suddenly feel an inexplicable and ineffable sense of joy, which is at once ardor and peace. It is a moment of buoyancy; all is happiness within you and around you; and you wish your present state might last forever.

That moment of exaltation was our presence. You have not been able to see the aura about you; but attentive watchers have recognized it. And the childish, adult or wrinkled hand which offers you a rose, or a heavy bunch of purple grapes, is extended towards the passing gods that you are.

Money is not what they want from you, but a friendly glance at the house, the child's cheek, or the pig grunting at its trough; the presence of happiness is always a benediction.

I gave the fisherman who had fed us the greatest gift it seemed to me possible to make him; not sudden wealth, not honors, not high functions, nor even a name in legend to commemorate our meeting; I made him "the happy Fisherman," living in harmony with the elements, content with the sunlight, the sand, the movement of the eternal sea, and able to perform the act of fishing excellently well; I endowed him with that physical and mental health which permits a man, no matter what his position in the terrestrial realm, to feel that he is a king; I wanted him throughout his days to be satisfied with being, not Someone or Something, but simply with Being, before sinking, mind and body together, and without excessive dread, into an ashy torpor, like a fire waning and dying on a beach.

The happy Fisherman certainly does not make the world progress—your human world, I mean; and yet he is necessary to its movement, for if he is not its impulse, he is its equipoise. He is always there to reveal their love to lovers, and to show conquerors another facet of truth.

*The Spring Beneath
the Pines.
The Cuckoo.
The Engagement.*

And it was that night I made Hera a present
of the stars; that is to say, I offered to share my celestial
power with her.

How did it happen? Well, in the first place because
we were in love, and were honest enough to tell each
other so as soon as we knew it. That was the first and
essential reason. And also because we mutually encouraged each other in the illusion, which is indispensable to all great decisions in love, that all the days
before us would resemble the one we had just lived.

The rest was merely conjuncture.

Do not believe the story that I failed to violate Hera,
and that she yielded to me only on my promising to
make her queen of the world. Those who have told
you that fable no doubt wanted an excuse for their
own weaknesses.

It can happen in love that we are refused what we
ask; but we are never obliged to give more than we
wish. And I would never have chosen for wife a goddess who had proposed so vulgar a bargain.

Of course, for a moment, we danced the natural ballet in which two mutually attracted forces each asserts its own principle before blending with the other, so as to give greater value and luster to the fusion itself.

When we left the Fisherman, we went to lie in a pine-wood where a warm spring flowed; Hera wished to bathe in it. Was this not to show me that she desired to purify herself before making love, while at the same time offering herself wholly to my gaze? There exists an evident correspondence between the female and water, as between the male and fire.

Kneeling in the very issue of the spring, Hera allowed the flowing crystal of the water to trickle down her ivory arms. I gazed at her superb body, which gave promise not only of delight but of vigorous children. And I suddenly felt a desire to watch her without her knowing I was doing so. I disappeared.

First, she looked round for me. Then, shivering, she moved away from the spring, and gazed anxiously up into the sky. It was the hour when the light was beginning to fade; the wheel of the sun's chariot was sinking below the horizon, and Aphrodite had just reappeared, bedizened with the cold gems I had given her the night before.

Aphrodite! There, indeed, was a conjuncture. Had it not been for Hera, I might have returned to the delirious goddess for another night of exhausting insomnia. But without Aphrodite, would I have appreciated Hera's solid virtues so much?

Anxious at my disappearance, Hera spoke to the

pines. The pine is a tree that talks. At the slightest breeze, its needles start quivering and whispering like a thousand tongues. One must know how to listen to the pines.

"Where is Zeus?" Hera asked. "Where has he gone?"

But the pines became my accomplices.

"We do not know, we have not seen him," they murmured. "Wait for him and touch him by your patience."

Then Hera sat down thoughtfully on the carpet of dry needles, knowing that her whole destiny as a goddess was at stake at that moment.

And then a bird, a springtime cuckoo, cold, shivering, shabby, its grey feathers all ruffled, came and perched beside her; it hopped about awkwardly on its yellow legs, and uttered its monotonous cry.

Hera smiled.

"Poor, frozen, unhappy little bird," she said compassionately, "from what nest have you fallen?"

She picked up the bird, which seemed quite tame, and placed it between her breasts to warm it. As soon as I found myself so well placed, I assumed my most virilely divine form. But Hera, closing her hands, retained my desire a prisoner there.

"Did you really think, brother tease, that I had not recognized you?" she said. "Your disguise had verisimilitude, but you were really shivering overmuch for the season. And why did you assume the appearance of the most unfaithful bird in the whole of creation? Do you think I am so ignorant as not to know what the cuckoo is like? It shows perseverance only in calling to its mate; but as soon as it has paired with her, it abandons her, leaving her no other recourse than to lay little orphans, who are destined to become as wicked as their father, in borrowed nests."

"Hera, Hera, my voluble sister," I replied, "do you not realize that I assumed that particular form precisely to show that the fickle bird simply wanted to be trapped?"

Hera became serious again.

"Zeus, Zeus, I know that from the moment I belong to you, I shall never be able to part from you again."

Nothing male in the universe can remain insensitive to these sorts of declaration. Oh, how different Hera was from Aphrodite, who asserted that I would never be able to part from her!

"I know," she went on, "that other goddesses will want to seduce you and will succeed. I am resigned to it, however much it makes me suffer. You are the king of day and light; your brightness will be in demand on every side. But, I beseech you, give others only the hours of the day, and reserve your nights for me."

"If you gratify my nights, beautiful Hera, what need shall I have to seek for other pleasures and other loves during the day?"

One says these things, all these things—before. And one believes them. And this is how it must be.

"But you must know," I went on, "that I no longer have any part of the world to give you. My brothers have the sea, the metals and the dead. Memory possesses recollection, and Athena reason. The arts have been distributed among the Muses; and I have left the precious stones on Aphrodite's fingers. . . ."

"I ask nothing more of you," she said, "than to keep me for always."

Well, I clearly had to make up my mind to what I desired. "Take a wife," wise Oceanus had said. The moment had come to choose between an engagement or an eternal quest, the chain or the desert.

I happily accepted the chain and replied: "For always."

For such engagements, my sons, must be undertaken only in happiness, in the certainty of happiness. For regret comes soon enough! And if you are touched by regret at the very instant of binding yourself, then prefer the desert. It offers more resources than you might suppose; it is criss-crossed by the paths of travelers moving towards some work or some unique conquest. On occasion, one may even travel for a stage in company with another, in twin solitudes.

But this is not a state suitable to kings, nor to anyone who has to govern a community. Beware, mortals, of solitary princes; it is from among them that tyrants are recruited.

So Hera was to become my wife. She would have nothing of her own, unless it were me; that is to say, she would share everything with me. Reigning over the sleep of the Day, she became the ruler and mistress of the Night, till the end of time.

The Divine Nuptials.
The Four Terms
of Destiny.

Never, till then, had the first embraces of a divine couple been the occasion for special celebrations. When gods and goddesses united, their nuptials caused rejoicing to no one but themselves. I wanted ours to be a festival for the whole world.

I summoned Iris before dawn; she set off post-haste with my message, and her tracks, when day broke, had woven a basket of rainbows about the Earth.

Iris said to the gods: "Zeus invites you to his wedding. There has been the assembly of power; there has been the assembly of famine; the assembly of happiness will be held today."

Using light breezes, I had the clouds blown away from Olympus, so that men might be able to see us from below; and I ordered a second throne to be placed beside mine.

Long processions of gods came from every part of the horizon. Fauns, dryads and naiads, emerging from the rivers, lakes and woods, came skipping and dancing. Oceanus and the beautiful Tethys, calm and smiling, were joined on their way by their innumerable children. Also from the sea came old Nereus and the charming Doris, followed by seventy-six Nereids; the seventy-seventh, Amphitrite, came with Poseidon who had his numerous personal suite of marine tutelary spirits. Even my brother Hades had agreed to come up from his kingdom of the Infernal Regions; and Persephone, for whom this was the beginning of her annual stay on Earth, guided the steps of her blind husband. Our mother Rhea was naturally present; but why did she insist on wearing mourning on such an occasion?

When the gods had filled the vast amphitheater of the mountains, and the chariot of the Sun had risen into the spring sky, Hera and I came forward, while the Muses sang the most ravishing music in chorus.

Clothed in white veils, Hera carried the rose pomegranate of nuptials in one hand, and in the other an ivory scepter on which a cuckoo was perched, so as to show everyone that she had tamed the fickle bird. Her pet peacock strutted beside her, proudly spreading his ocellate tail.

Hera, who till now had always been so reserved, indeed modest, assumed so haughty a demeanor, and her eyes shone with such a light of triumph, that I felt somewhat afraid for the future. However, it was up to me to see that I remained the master. I had donned my golden crown, and carried in my hand my sheaf of thunderbolts; the eagle, the royal bird, was perched on my shoulder. Some mockers said that we appeared to be walking in an aviary. But I can assure you we were very splendid.

The Seasons and the Graces formed our escort; the

nymphs strewed fresh flowers before us; the Hesperides, come from their distant garden, had brought a basket full of golden apples as a present to the bride.

And so, as you can see, my daughters showed Hera no hostility; indeed, far from taking umbrage at her new dignity, they participated in her joy. To have won the affection of the children of my former mistresses was a proof of Hera's intelligence. This is how a good wife behaves: she marries even her husband's past.

The assembled gods showed a moment's surprise when they saw a queen enthroned before them, for that was indeed what it was. The day before Hera had possessed no individual power, but now she was appearing suddenly in the first place. And she was so beautiful, so majestic, so naturally royal, while her happiness was so apparent that, enthusiasm succeeding to astonishment, the gods rose as one man to acclaim her. I had indubitably chosen well!

But I signed to Athena to come and occupy her usual place on the other side of my throne, where she stood holding the spear and Aegis, so as to show that I intended to maintain reason.

Then Themis came up to me and asked: "Is it true that you have promised Hera that she shall be your wife for always?"

"Yes," I replied.

And I added: "Does the law forbid it?"

"In this domain," Themis said, "it is your promise which makes the law."

Then, turning to Hera, she said: "Have you promised Zeus to be his wife for always?"

"Yes," Hera replied.

"In that case," Themis said, "the gods are witnesses to the fact that you are united."

She had been my second love, but she showed no approval, blame or regret. She was impassively stating the fact.

But Metis, Demeter and Memory were less self-controlled.

"I was too prudent," the first seemed to be saying.

"I was too ingenuous and spontaneous," the second thought.

"I was too old for him," my dear aunt Memory said to herself.

And there were many glances exchanged among the goddesses betraying regret, envy or disappointment.

For, by the fact of this reciprocal engagement which, from being made in public, acquired the force of law, any goddess who tried from now on to attract my love would be stealing something from Hera; and none of them, even if successful, would be able to avoid the implicitly inferior position of him who steals in relation to him who has. And this was Hera's triumph.

May those of you, my sons, for whom this institution has not always proved satisfactory, forgive me; we had invented marriage.

Aphrodite, all starry, smiled at everyone to prove that nothing could deprive her of the supremacy of beauty; but one could guess that she was sore at heart.

From where came that sob which for an instant reached my ears across the distant vales of memory? I leaned down. It was poor Eurynome with her fish's tail gazing up at Olympus and seeing her vain dreams being fulfilled for another.

And that light figure appearing on the summits and slipping through the rows of the gods, carrying a curved horn from which a thousand fruits were pouring? Dear little Amaltheia, forever adolescent, you too were there.

On the Earth, the descendants of King Melisseus and of King Celeus, and many other princes who followed their example, made great and sumptuous sacrifices in our honor. Many were the fat oxen, their horns garlanded with leaves; many were the thick-fleeced sheep slaughtered on the purified stones of altars; and many were the turning spits from which odors, spiced with thyme, laurel and rosemary, rose to rejoice our nostrils and nourish our immaterial entrails! And the golden chickens and the tender pigeons, and the hot cakes of well-ground wheat, and cheeses with appetizing odors that had been kept all winter, and freshly made ones, all milky and mixed with honey! Oh, my sons, what abundance and what succulence were there!

Among so many scents, I recognized without difficulty the aroma of the fish the happy Fisherman was dedicating to us on a fire of fennel, as he sat alone on the beach; and of all these offerings this one was far from giving me the least pleasure.

But the noise of the feasting going on below was almost beginning to drown the sound of ours; for hydromel, which is called ambrosia when we partake of it, was flowing without stint in the first clay cups;

and the subtle forces it released were turning the heads of both men and gods.

I looked at my beautiful Hera. I thought of the children we would have. From my throne, I gazed at the great feast which was taking place on Olympus, and at the innumerable feasts of men which, shadows of that of the gods, were repeated to infinity. I saw the fauns smile at the water-nymphs; I saw young mortals seeking the glances of future lovers and dreaming of nuptials in the image of ours. How many kisses did the bushes shelter that night and how many troths did the springs hear plighted!

I was happy; for my happiness, mortals, is nourished by your dreams.

"Hera," I said, leaning towards her, "we shall have sons. I would like our oldest to be robust, as inventive as he is hardworking, and that he should assist me in works of fire so as to forge for men the numerous gifts I intend conferring on them."

It was the image of Hephaestus, the divine workman, Hephaestus, the god of Work, that was already forming in my mind.

But Hera, too, was dreaming; she was dreaming of a son, who would be handsome, dominating and a conqueror, whose victories would fill her with pride. Did she put too much ardor into this dream? The fruit of it was Ares, the god of Battles.

"I also wish," I went on, "so as to immortalize this day, that we should have a daughter born to us, who will preside over future feasts, organize them, and pour out the divine beverages which induce love; I want her to be forever virginal, the image of what you are at this moment preserved for all eternity. We shall call her Hebe."

"You are thinking of gods and men," Hera said, "but I want to think of goddesses and women. I have long heard them groan at the pains of childbirth. Our union will be of eternal benefit to them, if we have a goddess who will be the protectress of Childbirth, relieving the pains of parturition and assisting happy deliveries. Ilithye will be her name. And thanks to her both mortals and immortals will be better assured of perpetuating their race. . . ."

Birth, Feasting, Work and War; was it not in these four terms that the whole destiny of my descendants was being composed—your destiny, my sons, which revolves incessantly on these four pillars?

I could imagine the infinite succession of your generations. Yes, I was as happy as a king can be.

Night was falling. I sought to catch Hecate's three glances and saw that she approved me.

On your Earth, libations, singing and dancing continued. And the gods were also singing on Olympus. Accompanied once again by the escort of Graces, Seasons and Muses, Hera and I withdrew to the vast golden bed that had been made ready for us; and, so as to conceal us, Night spread like a peacock's tail, the Night of a million stars of which Hera was henceforth the sovereign.

Envoy.

Let us part, mortals my sons, on this happy memory. For I perceive that I have been talking for a long time, for longer than you are accustomed to listen. The chariot of the Sun has sunk into the sea; this is the hour at which I go to join Hera as I have done for so many thousands of years. Alas, every night is not a nuptial night!

I leave it to him who is a descendant of my race and has recognized my voice to translate my words into your language. If his narrative seems to you clumsy, rough, and sometimes obscure and contradictory, do not reproach him, nor accuse me. The limited human tongue does not possess all the modulations of the language of the gods. It is only within yourselves, as a result of contemplating or meditating on the sacred words, that you may at moments succeed in hearing the music of the spheres.

Perhaps tomorrow, in the valley of Delphi with its flaming rocks, or beneath the quivering pines of Olympia, among the relics of your most beautiful works, or again on some beach in the golden bay of Nauplia, I, Zeus, king of gods, god of men, may return to continue your history and mine.